THE
RAILWAY
PUZZLE
BOOK

THE RAILWAY PUZZLE BOOK

Will Adams

· A SILVER LINK BOOK ·
from
The NOSTALGIA Collection

First published in 2004

British Library Cataloguing in Publication Data

A catalogue record for this book is available from the British Library.

ISBN 1 85794 243 4

Silver Link Publishing Ltd
The Trundle
Ringstead Road
Great Addington
Kettering
Northants NN14 4BW

Tel/Fax: 01536 330588
email: sales@nostalgiacollection.com
Website: www.nostalgiacollection.com

Printed and bound in Great Britain

® RAILWAY BOOK CLUB
www.railway.co.uk

Preface

by the Editor, the Railway Book Club

One of the most satisfying parts of being interested in railways is knowing a lot about them. They are worth knowing about, because over the last 200 years, with an apex 100 years ago, they have been one of the prime movers in human progress. The only people who could keep them going were the railwaymen who knew every detail of their construction and operation, and in admiring their achievement we want to understand those details ourselves.

For 25 years the Railway Book Club has been distributing this knowledge with the co-operation of authors and publishers. Now comes the time to put it to the test. How much do you know about the railways? We invited Silver Link Publishing and Will Adams, compiler of the previous *Railway Puzzle Book*, to ask the questions for our own Silver Jubilee. We hope that by being members of the Club, your knowledge has improved. Try the puzzles and see!

Introduction

Happy are those who can combine their hobbies with their jobs, so as a lifelong railway enthusiast, and a professional puzzle compiler as well as editor with nostalgia book publisher Silver Link Publishing/Past & Present Publishing, I am very grateful to the Railway Book Club for giving me once again the opportunity to indulge in that combination. I'd also like to thank noted railway author and publisher Geoff Body for casting his expert eye over the contents, although if any gremlins do manage to slip through, they're of my own making.

This is not an exam paper. There are no scores. You won't graduate with First Class Honours in Rivet-Counting if you can answer every clue and question. Rather it's intended to be a fun way to see what nuggets of trivia you can dredge up from the back of your mind, and if you are stumped for an answer, I hope also that the puzzles will provide plenty of 'Well, I didn't know that…' moments.

I haven't delved deep into the minutiae of railway history and technology. By and large the puzzles cover the classic nostalgia period – say, the last 40 or so years – and for reference I've used the books on my own shelves (many of which are, of course, Railway Book Club titles!). I hope you have to refer frequently to your own collection – that's half the fun. I also hope that in some cases the process of solving the puzzles will be enjoyable in itself, regardless of how much you have to look up.

In short, I've tried to provide a loose-coupled, mixed goods type of book, the puzzles marshalled in no particular order, with a huffing and puffing compiler at the head, who's very pleased to have completed the job and can now run light to the local hostelry to be fuelled and watered. Or something.

A mixed load !

Will Adams

Pioneers

When all the answers are in place, the first column will contain the surname of a locomotive pioneer whose most famous achievement took place 200 years ago this year.

1	T	R	A	M	R	O	A	D		
2	R	A	I	N	H	I	L	L		
3	E	D	G	E	H	I	L	L		
4	V	I	G	N	O	L	E	S		
5	I	S	A	M	B	A	R	D		
6	T	H	A	M	E	S				
7	H	E	D	L	E	Y				
8	I	N	V	I	C	T	A			
9	C	O	O	K						
10	K	I	L	L	I	N	G	W	O	R	T	H

1   Hall's ___, horse-worked system in South Wales, opened in 1809 (8)
2   Location of a famous Liverpool & Manchester Railway locomotive trials in 1829 (8)
3   Liverpool station built in 1836 for the Liverpool & Manchester Railway (4,4)
4   Charles ___, engineer who worked on the Liverpool & Manchester and Midland Counties Railways, and had a type of rail named after him (8)
5   Brunel's first name … (8)
6   … and the river he and his father tunnelled beneath in 1823-43 (6)
7   William ___, builder of the early colliery loco *Puffing Billy* of 1813 (6)
8   Name of the preserved Canterbury & Whitstable Railway 0-4-0 of 1830 (7)
9   Thomas ___, organiser of the first railway excursion in July 1841 (4)
10   Colliery for which George Stephenson built his first locomotive, *Blucher* (12)

Preserved in steam

1 Which is Britain's longest standard-gauge heritage railway, at 20 miles?

2 The perennial *Nasturtium officinale* is associated with the Mid-Hants Railway – in what way?

3 Which famous battle of 1485 is commemorated in the name of the Battlefield Line at Shackerstone?

4 At which railway centre is the rebuilt Oxford Rewley Road LNWR station now a Visitor Centre?

5 What is the present-day name of the line that used to be known as the Dart Valley Railway?

6 Which preservation scheme is based at Blunsdon station, not yet having reached either of the places in its title?

7 Which preserved line features Greet Tunnel?

8 What is the terminus of the preserved branch line that leaves the former GWR main line at Cholsey & Moulsford station?

9 Which railway centre used to be known simply as 81E?

10 Which preserved line uses part of what was originally the Severn & Wye Railway?

11 Which line features almost 3 miles at 1 in 49, which replaced a horse-worked incline at 1 in 10?

12 Which preserved line was opened in 1882, closed in 1955, re-opened in 1956, closed again in 1958, and re-opened by a preservation group in 1968?

13 Which major preserved line's southern terminus is on the site of the former Belgrave & Birstall station, but has a different name today?

14 Which line is associated with artist David Shepherd?

15 Which preserved line began life as the Rother Valley Railway, the first line to be authorised under the Light Railways Act 1896?

16 Which lines features the picturesquely named Coleslogget Halt?

17 Which preservation company is hoping one day to be reconnected to the main line at Worgret Junction?

18 Which preserved line's inaugural train in June 1977 was worked by a former Swedish State Railway 2-6-2 tank locomotive?

19 Which line in Devon nominally links two places one of which has never been directly served by a railway, even in pre-preservation days?

20 Which Welsh preserved line begins and ends beside the River Dee?

World celebration!

Answer the following geographical clues and enter them in the grid,
where their initial letters will spell out a something they all have in common,
and which is also relevant to this book.

1	J	A	M	A	C	I	A	
2	U	L	S	T	E	R		
3	B	A	H	A	M	A	S	
4	I	N	D	O	R	E		
5	L	E	I	N	S	T	E	R
6	E	I	R	E				
7	E	D	W	A	R	D		

1 West Indies island, capital Kingston (7)
2 Northern Irish province (6)
3 West Indies island group, capital Nassau (7)
4 Indian city and former princely state that sounds as though it's not outside! (6)
5 Ancient kingdom and province of… (8)
6 …the Irish Republic (4)
7 Prince ___ Island, province of SE Canada, capital Charlottetown (6)

Crossword No 1

Across

1 Number of the M&GNR station between Bourne and Spalding! (6)

4 Name on eight GWR 'King' nameplates (6)

9 The 'Long ___', enginemen's nickname for the Settle & Carlisle line (4)

10 ___ *Athol*, 'A3' No 60058 (5)

11 ___ *Tryfan*, Welsh Highland Railway 0-4-2T single Fairlie (4)

12 *Sans* ___, Class 86/2 No 86214 (6)

13 Bank between Carlisle and Carstairs (8)

14 *The South Wales* ___, 'Castle' No 4037 (9)

16 ___ *of Badenoch*, Class 60 No 60100 (4)

17 '___ truck', single-axle truck before or behind a steam loco's driving wheels (4)

18 *Royal* ___ ___, No D9000 (5,4)

22 Exeter station (2,6)

23 'Warship' No D600 (6)
25 Famous Settle & Carlisle station (4)
26 and 27 Former signal box between the tunnels outside London King's Cross (5,4)
28 Word following Baker, Curzon and Princes in station names (6)
29 'Jubilee' No 45586 (6)

Down

1 Name of the new loco being built by the A1 Steam Locomotive Trust (7)
2 *Golden* ___, 'A4' No 60023 (5)
3 Descriptive of Robert Stephenson's bridge across the Menai Strait (7)
5 ___ *School*, 'V2' No 60860 (6)
6 Surname of a family of 19th-century GWR Locomotive Engineers (9)
7 GCR station between Sheffield and Penistone (7)
8 GWR 4-6-0 No 7028 (7,6)
15 Location of the famous locomotive works known as 'The Plant' (9)
17 ___ Bar, ECML station in Hertfordshire (7)
19 'A3' No 60059 (7)
20 ___ *Hall*, No 4922 (7)
21 River giving its name to a famous Settle & Carlisle viaduct (6)
24 'A3' No 60084 (5)

Odd junction out

The picturesque name of the signal box forming the answer to 26 and 27 across belied its location in a smoky cutting north of King's Cross. Here are some more unusual junction signal box names. In each group of three, two are real places – can you identify the made-up name?

1 Thingley Junction, Wotsitt Junction, Hoo Junction

2 Dragon Junction, Bo Peep Junction, Cat & Fiddle Junction

3 Two Ways Junction, Three Signal Bridge Junction, Junction Road Junction

4 Cuckoo Junction, Sparrow Junction, Dove Junction

5 Incline Junction, Over Junction, Uphill Junction

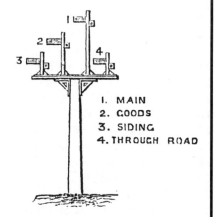

1. MAIN
2. GOODS
3. SIDING
4. THROUGH ROAD

Crossword No 2

Across

9 The ___ ___, GWR loco, Britain's first 'Pacific' (5,4)

10 ___ Hill, station between Manchester and Wigan (5)

11 Duchess of ___, No 46228 (7)

12 ___ Abbey, 'Castle' No 5087 (7)

13 ___ Hill, the GWR's main Birmingham station (4)

14 'Britannia' No 70003 (4,6)

17 Kensington ___ Road, station that became Kensington Olympia in 1946 (7)

18 Word preceding *Pilot* and *Command* on two 'Battle of Britain' 'Pacifics' (7)

20 'A2/3' No 60529 (5,5)

23 D1, for example (4)

25 GWR 'Hall' No 4973, associated with George Carter and Jack Regan? (7)

26 City that had High Street, Riverside, St Thomas and Victoria stations (7)

28 'B1' No 61001 (5)

29 ___ Junction, station for the Blaenau Ffestiniog line (9)

Down

1 *Castell ___/Ogmore Castle*, bilingual Class 56 nameplate (4)

2 ___ Loop, ECML avoiding line between Wood Green and Langley Junction (8)

3 'Jubilee' No 45737 (5)

4 Station at the north end of the Kent & East Sussex Light Railway (8)

5 'EM1' electric loco No 26056 (6)

6 City that had steam sheds at Dalry Road and Haymarket (9)

7 Station between Leicester and Loughborough (6)

8 Kings on the GER, South on the M&GNR (4)

13 Baron ___ of Shortlands, Chairman and President of the LMS Executive, 1927-41 (5)

15 ___ *Hydro*, Class 47 No 47319 (5)

16 Seaside station at Ryde, IOW (9)

18 ___ *Hall*, No 5981 (8)

19 ___ *Steelmaster*, Class 37 No 37078 (8)

21 ___ Street, intermediate station on the GCR's Grendon Underwood Junction-Ashendon Junction link (6)

22 'B1' No 61016 (6)

24 'Jubilee' No 45675 (5)

25 'Top ___', King's Cross steam loco depot (4)

27 ___ Wen, LNWR/Cambrian junction east of Pwllheli (3)

On the streets

Two 'Street' station names were featured in the crossword above.
Can you identify the cities or towns that contained the following stations?

1 Moor Street (GWR)

2 Great Moor Street (LNWR)

3 Arkwright Street (GCR)

4 Buchanan Street (Caledonian)

5 Foregate Street (GWR)

6 Clegg Street (LYR)

7 Adam Street (Rhymney)

8 Bolton Street (LYR)

9 Market Street (MR)

10 Clarence Street and Crane Street (GWR)

The Big Four: GWR

1 Which famous GWR structure carries the inscription 'I. K. BRUNEL ENGINEER 1859'?

2 What nickname did the GWR give itself as a result of frequent use by monarchy travelling between Paddington and Windsor?

3 In 1935 new stock was provided for the famous 'Cornish Riviera Express', taking its name from an important GWR event of that year. What was it?

4 Which GWR train held world speed records in 1929, 1931 and 1932?

5 The first 'Castle' Class locomotive of 1923 was exhibited alongside the LNER's *Flying Scotsman* at the British Empire Exhibition – what was its name?

6 Which appropriately named 'Castle' became the regular Royal Train engine after King George V drove it to Swindon station following a Royal Visit to the Works in 1924?

7 The first 'King' 4-6-0, *King George V*, went to America in 1927 to celebrate the centenary of which US railroad?

8 In 1935 *King Henry VII* and *Manorbier Castle* were the subject of an experiment – in what?

9 The 1934 prototype AEC diesel railcar No 1 operated between Paddington and which other station?

10 A book of humorous drawings, *Railway Ribaldry*, was published to mark the GWR's centenary. Which artist was responsible?

11 In 1934 that at College Wood, on the Falmouth branch, was the last to be rebuilt – the last what?

12 In the 1930s 75 GWR goods services had names, including the 'Bacca' from Bristol to London, the 'Tinman' from Margam to Bordesley, and the 'Sauce' from Paddington to which city?

13 In 1924 'Saint' Class *Saint Martin* was altered by C. B. Collett to become the prototype for which large class of GWR 4-6-0s?

14 Almost 170 of which type of facility were opened by the GWR between 1927 and 1935?

15 What was the name of the last class of GWR 4-6-0 passenger locos to be introduced, in 1945?

16 The last General Manager of the GWR was vehemently opposed to nationalisation and refused the post of first chairman of the Railway Executive. Who was he?

17 Which was the GWR's largest steam shed, probably the largest in Britain, if not the world?

18 Which GWR General Manager, who retired in 1929, mastered Braille when overcome by blindness, enabling him to write his autobiography in 1954, two years before his death?

19 Which well-known GWR publication ran to 1,000 pages in 1927, and sold 200,000 copies each year from 1928 to 1931?

20 In 1930 26,000 GWR employees and their families travelled on the specially arranged fleet of trains from Swindon Works to the seaside. What was the nickname of this annual event?

Branching out

Can you match up these GWR intermediate branch-line stations
with their respective termini?

1	Aston Rowant	Cardigan
2	Blue Anchor	Fairford
3	Carbis Bay	Helston
4	Crymmych Arms	Hemyock
5	Lustleigh	Minehead
6	Manorbier	Moretonhampstead
7	Nancegollan	Tetbury
8	Rodmarton Platform	Pembroke Dock
9	Uffculme	St Ives
10	Witney	Watlington

Crossword No 3

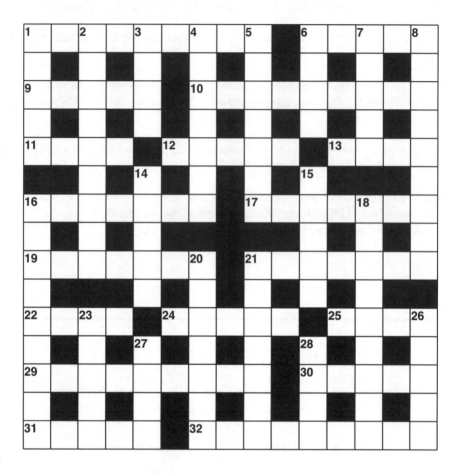

Across

1 Terminus of a GER branch from Saxmundham (9)

6 *Saint ___*, 'A1' No 60145 (5)

9 *Firth of ___*, 'Britannia' No 70050 (5)

10 and 15 down Name carried by several engines, from a GWR broad-gauge 'Iron Duke' to Class 87 No 87024 (4,2,3,5)

11 Station between Norwich and Great Yarmouth (4)

12 Loco assisting a train engine (5)

13 GNR station between Hatfield and Dunstable (4)

16 Headquarters of the Keighley & Worth Valley Railway (7)

17 ___ Hall marshalling yard, Crewe (7)

19 *Western ___*, No D1049 (7)

21 ___ & Holyhead Railway, incorporated in 1844 and worked by the LNWR until absorbed in 1859 (7)
22 *Royal* ___, name given to LMS No 6100 in 1927 (4)
24 Surname of the British composer commemorated by Class 50 No 50007 (5)
25 The 'U' of DMU (4)
29 *Princess* ___, preserved LMS 'Pacific' No 6201 (9)
30 ___ *Glyndwr*, Vale of Rheidol Railway No 7 (5)
31 Welsh Highland Railway station south of Caernarfon (5)
32 ___ *Hall*, No 6952 (9)

Down

1 D234 (5)
2 Preserved 'Castle' No 5051 (9)
3 and 6 down Settle & Carlisle tunnel north of Ribblehead (4,4)
4 'Jubilee' No 45639 (7)
5 *Lord* ___, 'Britannia' No 70001 (7)
6 See 3 down
7 ___ Bridge, GNofSR station north-east of Boat of Garten (5)
8 'A2/3' No 60520 (4,5)
14 *City of* ___, famous preserved GWR 4-4-0 No 3440 (5)
15 See 10 across
16 North London Line tunnel west of Gospel Oak (8)
18 Preserved GWR No 5972 (5,4)
20 Former Leeds steam shed, 55A (7)
21 Reputedly Britain's busiest Junction (7)
23 Large Welshpool & Llanfair Railway 2-6-2T No 5/15 (5)
26 Seaside station on the Pembroke Dock branch (5)
27 'Jubilee' No 45698 (4)
28 Raised location for the regulator valve above a steam loco's boiler (4)

Elgar enigma!

From the number of the 1990s Co-Co electric *Elgar*, subtract the TOPS number of the former D407 *Sir Edward Elgar*, then the number of 'Castle' 4-6-0 *Sir Edward Elgar*, then the number of letters on the latter's nameplate, then delete the first digit of the answer to reveal a building where Elgar's music is regularly heard. Where is it?

Crossword No 4

Across

8 D601 in 1958, and D435 in 1968, the latter preserved (3,5)

9 BR Standard 4-6-0 No 73116 (6)

10 Nickname for the concourse area at Paddington (4)

11 River bridged unsuccessfully by Thomas Bouch in the 1870s (3)

12 ___ Junction, Bucks meeting-place of the Metropolitan and LNWR (6)

13 Viaduct beside a quarry of the same name south-west of Okehampton (6)

15 *Royal* ___ *Corps*, 'Battle of Britain' No 34050 (8)

17 ___ *of Britain*, No D210 (7)

19 'Castle' No 5099, or 'Manor' No 7807 (7)

22 Welsh narrow-gauge railway, saved by a pioneering preservation organisation in 1951 (8)

24 'A1' No 60149 (6)

25 Loco-hauled Pullman Kitchen Car – perhaps coupled to Princess *Louise*? (6)

27 and 21 down Oddly named station near Sevenoaks (3,3,4)

28 and 29 GWR No 6011 (4,5,1)

30 GER station between Sudbury and Bury St Edmunds (8)

Down

1 *Village of ___*, ARC Class 59 No 59104 (5,3)

2 Tiny 18-inch-gauge 0-4-0ST used by the L&YR in Horwich Works (4)

3 ___ & Barnstaple Railway (6)

4 Builder of the 1962 Type 1 centre-cab diesel locos in the D8500 series (7)

5 'A3' No 60068 (3,5)

6 ___ Green, London-High Wycombe line station (4)

7 ___ *Abbey*, 'Castle' No 5091, or 'Grange' No 6850 (6)

14 Headquarters city of the Midland Railway (5)

16 ___ *1893-1993*, name carried by Class 47 No 47085 (1,1,1,1,1)

18 D231 (8)

20 *Peninsular and ___ SN Co*, 'Merchant Navy' No 35006 (7)

21 See 27 across

23 Receptacle beneath a steam loco's grate (6)

24 D600 (6)

26 ___ & Manifold Valley Light Railway (4)

28 ___ & East Sussex Railway (4)

First name terms

The last two clues above involve identifying the missing word in railway company names. Can you supply the missing place names from the following?

1	_____	& Swansea Bay Railway
2	_____	& Carlisle Railway
3	_____	& Montgomeryshire Light Railway
4	_____	& South London Railway
5	_____	& Swannington Railway
6	_____	& Wyre Joint Railway
7	_____	& Knot (sic) End Railway
8	_____	& West Junction Railway
9	_____	& Upwell Tramway
10	_____	& Machrihanish Light Railway

Tunnel vision

When the names of the tunnels are in position in the columns of the grid, the letters in the marked row will spell out the name of another, on the East Coast Main Line.

1   On the Settle & Carlisle line, between Garsdale and Ais Gill summit (8)
2   Also on the S&C, between Settle and Dent, 1½ miles long (4,4)
3   Between Leeds and Harrogate, more than 2 miles long (8)
4   Between Peak Forest and Chapel-en-le-Frith, nearly 1¾ miles long (4,5)
5   ___ Weston, on the LSWR main line between Gillingham and Templecombe (8)
6   On the S&C again, between the station of the same name and Langwathby (8)
7   On the North London line, between Gospel Oak and Finchley Road (9)
8   On the South Coast, between St Leonards Warrior Square and the seaside town station of the same name, 788 yards long (8)
9   Between Leeds and Shipley on the former Midland route (8)
10 Mount ___, just 230 yards long between answer 8 and Ore (8)

Bridges

1 On which preserved line did a lady called Victoria Bridge help to re-open the newly refurbished Victoria Bridge in April 2004?

2 Which city's Central station is approached from each end via the King Edward and High Level bridges?

3 Dunford Bridge station is at the eastern end of which 3-mile-long tunnel?

4 Bridge of Orchy, Roy Bridge and Spean Bridge are all found on which line?

5 London-bound trains used to pass in opposite directions at Cowley Bridge Junction. Where is it, and why was this seeming contradiction the case?

6 Which Midlands county town's former LNWR Bridge Street station closed in 1964?

7 Days Bridge Junction was just east of which major GWR station?

8 Devil's Bridge is the terminus of which narrow-gauge railway?

9 Which London terminus was approached via Grosvenor Bridge, the first railway bridge to cross the Thames in the London area?

10 When the Royal Border Bridge at Berwick was opened by Queen Victoria in 1850, its engineer was offered, but declined, a knighthood. Who was he?

11 Sankey Viaduct, the earliest large masonry viaduct, was constructed in 1830 for which railway?

12 In 1836 which railway approached London built entirely on 3¾ miles of bridges comprising 878 arches using 60 million bricks?

13 What do Selby, Trowse and Hawarden bridges have in common?

14 Brunel's tubular bridge construction technique seen in the Royal Albert Bridge at Saltash was used earlier on a much smaller bridge across the Wye at which town?

15 Stephenson's tubular bridge technique seen in the Britannia Bridge across the Menai Strait was tested earlier in a bridge across which North Wales river in the town of the same name?

16 The former road/rail swingbridge at Sutton Bridge in Lincolnshire was used by which pre-Grouping railway company?

17 Which famous bridge was the subject of John Prebble's 1956 book *The High Girders?*

18 Norton Bridge Junction north of Stafford is the divergence point of the former LNWR line to Crewe and the former North Staffordshire line to which town?

19 Despite its name, Highbridge was the location of a level crossing between the GWR and which other pre-Grouping company?

20 Connel Ferry Bridge, the country's second largest steel cantilever bridge, across the mouth of Loch Etive, represented the beginning of which former Caledonian Railway branch?

Level crossings

Can you identify these four two-word locations, one from each of the 'Big Four', from the clues and the initials of the owning company? The vertical word is the first.

I Junction for Helston

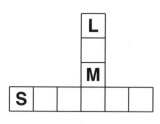

2 Liverpool

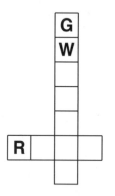

3 Junction for Haverhill and Bury St Edmunds

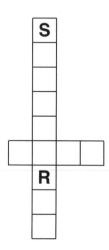

4 Junction for the East Kent Railway

Summit search

The names of the 28 railway summits listed below are hidden in this grid of letters. The words may read backwards, forwards, up, down, or diagonally, but always in a straight line and never skipping letters. Not all the letters in the grid are used, while some are used more than once.

```
K N H U M B G L D H E R T W D O E
O D C E I L L I U M E I R R O C R
O E R C N N E K T I F W U O R D O
R D A O G A N S C H B I I C O T M
B L M R R T O A H O M P G S W E N
N E Y R A S G D L U T E A H H N I
R I T O V V L L A B E T I H W F A
A F N U E O E C N T R T A D S G T
H E U R K E H N D L R T T E E I S
S L O C H D E R S O L I I N B D G
T T C D A V A N P R O I N R T D H
O S A I N T D E E N O N G G O R N
K I R E N O T N I A D C F S O E H
E H R E N I L C N I Y E K C I L F
O W H O N I T O N L L I H A L A F
U R E W W A P E A K F O R E S T I
```

AIS GILL
BEATTOCK
CORRIEMUILLIE
CORROUR
COUNTY MARCH
DAINTON
DAVA
DRUIMUACHDAIR
DUTCHLANDS
FALAHILL

GLENOGLEHEAD
HEWISH
HONITON
INGRAVE
LICKEY INCLINE
LUIB
PEAK FOREST
RAVEN'S ROCK
SHAP

SHARNBROOK
SLOCHD
STAINMORE
STOKE
TALERDDIG
TRING
WHISTLEFIELD
WHITEBALL
WHITROPE

Crossword No 5

Across

9 ___ (Newport & South Wales) Dock & Railway Co (9)

10 *King* ___, BR Standard No 73111 (5)

11 *Western* ___, D1061 (5)

12 GWR station north of 22 across that inspired a famous poem by Edward Thomas (9)

13 SR Chief Mechanical Engineer who was formerly assistant to Gresley on the LNER (7)

14 'A3' No 60069 (7)

17 ___ Electronic Tokenless Block, modern signalling system on lightly used single lines (5)

19 *Sir Frank* ___, 'Patriot' No 45530 (3)

20 Woburn ___, station between Bedford and Bletchley (5)

21 Hertfordshire town with GER and GNR stations called Lock, Chase and Town (7)

22 GWR junction where the Oxford-Worcester and Banbury-Cheltenham lines crossed (7)

24 Station on the preserved South Devon Railway (9)

26 Crewe, Eastleigh or Doncaster, eg (5)

28 Three ___, Cambrian/GWR Junction south of Hay (5)

29 SR 'Schools' No 30936 (9)

Down

1 MR Gloucestershire junction for the Thornbury branch (4)

2 Somerset town that had Pen Mill, Town and Junction stations (6)

3 GCR's London terminus (10)

4 Name on the nameplates of both preserved GWR 'Kings' (6)

5 City that had Kingmoor, Canal and Upperby loco sheds (8)

6 Nickname of L&YR 0-4-0ST dock locos (4)

7 Paignton & Dartmouth Railway station, formerly junction for Brixham (8)

8 Name given to the annual employees' holiday outing from Swindon 26 across (4)

13 Edmund ___, Metropolitan Railway Bo-Bo electric loco No 7 (5)

15 Terminus of a short independent branch from Alne, NER, closed in 1948 (10)

16 Name of numerically the next 'Schools' after 29 across (5)

18 'Jubilee' No 45728, preserved Class 50 No 50049, and a GWR 'Platform' west of the Royal Albert Bridge (8)

19 Somerset town with GWR and S&DJR stations (8)

22 First station on the Windermere branch (6)

23 'A3' No 60109 (6)

24 Management committee formed in 1899 to operate two railway companies from London to Kent (1,1,1,1)

25 ___ Asiatic Company, 'Merchant Navy' No 35024 (4)

27 ___ Road and ___ Pool, LNWR stations in Birmingham – not the West End of London! (4)

Triple chance

The town providing the answer to 21 across had three stations identified by different names. Which places have or used to have the following stations?

1 City, Midland, Victoria

2 Midland, Central, Market Place

3 Central, City, Wellington

4 Victoria, Riverside, St Thomas

5 St Thomas, St David's, Queen Street

6 Lord Street, Chapel Street, St Luke's

7 St James, Malvern Road, Lansdown

8 Central, Harbour, West

9 Beach, South Town, Vauxhall

10 Esplanade, East, West

Railwaymen

1 Which company did Dr Beeching leave to join the British Transport Commission, and later return to?

2 Which engineer, who pioneered the use of concrete in railway civil engineering, including the famous Glenfinnan Viaduct of 1897, gained the nickname 'Concrete Bob'?

3 Which GWR Locomotive Superintendent was at the same time Conservative MP for Cricklade, between 1865 and 1885?

4 Which railway author succeeded Cecil J. Allen as writer of *The Railway Magazine's* 'Locomotive Practice and Performance' feature, contributing 264 articles between 1958 and 1980?

5 Which director, vice-chairman then chairman of the Great Eastern Railway between 1872 and 1922 is commemorated by a class of 4-4-0s of 1900?

6 What were the first two names of the GWR Chief Mechanical Engineer C. B. Collett?

7 The Midland Railway's James Allport was the first railway manager to receive which honour, in 1884?

8 Whose many inventions included an organ blower, steam hammer, revolving gun and improved earth closet, but is best remembered for his radial locomotive valve gear of 1879?

9 Which former Labour Minister of Transport became Chairman of British Rail in 1971?

10 Which American railway entrepreneur had the first names George Mortimer?

11 Which area of the railway business was the responsibility of Sir William Towle and his son Arthur on the Midland Railway and later the LMS between 1871 and 1945?

12 Which LNWR Locomotive Engineer was Mayor of Crewe in 1886-87 and left much of his considerable fortune to deserving causes in the district?

13 Which locomotive firebox innovation was first fitted by Matthew Kirtley on the Midland Railway?

14 H. A. Ivatt's locomotive No 990 of 1898 was the first of what type to appear in Britain?

15 Which LMS Locomotive Engineer was born in Swindon, the son of William Dean's confidential clerk, and served his apprenticeship in the works there from 1892, rising to Principal Assistant to Collett before leaving in 1932?

16 For 40 years (1851 to 1891) Sir Richard Moon was deputy chairman then chairman of which railway company?

17 Which engineer served his apprenticeship at Crewe under Bowen Cooke from 1909, was described in a 1970 biography as 'The Last Steam Locomotive Engineer', and died aged 100 in 1983?

18 Which famous railway photographer has the unusual distinction of having a road named after him, in Bath?

19 Which late railway author chronicled the preservation of the Talyllyn Railway in his 1953 book *Railway Adventure*, and has a loco on that railway named after him?

20 Which former Southern Railway general manager was the first chairman of the nationalised Railway Executive, and had a 'Battle of Britain' 'Pacific' named after him?

Sir names

All the following knights have been commemorated on locomotive nameplates, but in this puzzle their first names and surnames have been scrambled. Can you discover the correct pairings?

1   Sir Alexander Walker KCB

2   Sir Brian Wilson

3   Sir Christopher Milne

4   Sir Frederick McAlpine

5   Sir Henry Erskine-Hill

6   Sir Herbert Wren

7   Sir James Park

8   Sir Keith Johnson

9   Sir Murrough Robertson

10 Sir Robert Pile

Crossword No 6

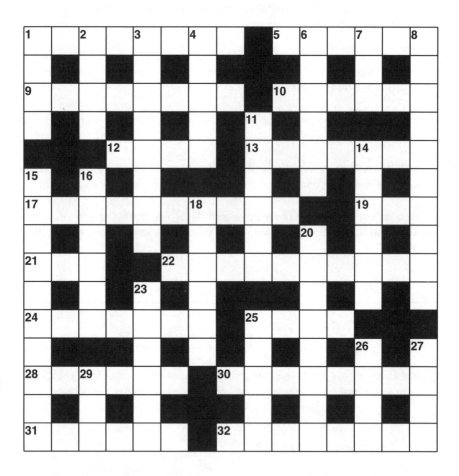

Across

1 Type of firebox with a flat-topped outer casing (8)
5 Rev W. Awdry's famous Tank Engine (6)
9 Settle & Carlisle line tunnel south of Garsdale (4,4)
10 ___ the Great, 'Britannia' No 70009 (6)
12 and 25 across Cromford & ___ ___ Railway (4,4)
13 Vale of ___ Railway, Welsh narrow-gauge line (7)
17 The ___ ___, No D9013 (5,5)
19 Guard's van with a driving cab, at the opposite end of a train from the loco (1,1,1)
21 Initials of Mr Maunsell, Southern Railway CME, 1923-37 (1,1,1)
22 Terminus of a GWR moorland branch from Yelverton (10)
24 'Jubilee' No 45554 (7)
25 See 12 across

28 'B1' No 61002 (6)

30 Station name once found in Barnstaple, Nottingham and Sheffield (8)

31 Hampstead ___, 14 down, Newbury & Southampton line station (6)

32 Somerset quarry after which No 56031 was named (8)

Down

1 Edward ___, Loco Superintendent of the London & Birmingham Railway (4)

2 Station at the southern end of the Longmoor Military Railway (4)

3 ___ *Hall*, No 5976 (8)

4 ___ *Assheton*, 'B1' No 61036 (5)

6 James ___, Loco, Carriage & Wagon Superintendent of the GER, 1885-1907 (6)

7 In short, a non-stop coal train on a circular route! (1,1,1)

8 Loco with its water supply carried over the boiler (6,4)

11 Neath & ___ Railway, GWR constituent from 1922 (6)

14 Railway Centre that is home to the Great Western Society (6)

15 'A1' No 60158 (10)

16 Circular device carried on an engine as authorisation to occupy a single line (6)

18 D212 (6)

20 Engineer giving his name to a type of five-nozzle blastpipe, used by Bulleid (8)

23 West Highland Line station south of Crianlarich (6)

25 Of a steam engine, to carry water droplets with the steam into the cylinders (5)

26 Robert W. ___, Chief Mechanical Engineer of the LSWR, 1912-22 (4)

27 Area of goods sidings (4)

29 Cornwall junction for the Newquay branch (3)

Back and forth

Nos 45554 and D212, mentioned above, both had 'palindromic' numberplates, ie the numbers were the same forwards and backwards. Can you provide palindromic numbers for the following named steam and diesel locomotives (TOPS numbers for the latter)?

1 *Great Western*, and …

2 … with an extra digit, *Coeur-de-Lion*

3 *Combe Martin*, and …

4 … using the same digits, *The Black Horse*

5 *King George I*, and …

6 … with an extra digit, *Sir Ralph Wedgwood* or *Great Gable*, and …

7 … with one digit changed, *Flying Fox*

8 *Manorbier Castle*, and …

9 … with an extra digit, *Collingwood*

10 *Post Restante*

Diesels

1 Which CME of the LMS introduced the first diesel-electric loco to run in Britain?

2 Which 1961 class of locos was powered by a diesel engine developed in the 1950s for use in fast naval patrol boats?

3 Which class of diesel locos derived its popular name from its hydraulic-mechanical transmission?

4 The Sulzer engines for the first ten 'Peaks' were built in which country?

5 Twenty-six of the 137 Class 45 'Peaks' carried names, mostly derived from which two former steam loco classes?

6 Which diesel loco, the first of its class, hauled the inaugural diesel-hauled passenger train between London Liverpool Street and Norwich in April 1958?

7 Which was the first Class 50 to pass into preservation, in August 1991?

8 The first ex-BR main-line diesel loco to be sold into preservation, in 1973, was from which Western Region class?

9 The last main-line diesel to be given a major overhaul at Swindon Works, and jointly the last of its class to be withdrawn, is now part of the National Collection. Which class?

10 The 510 Class 47s were built at Brush's Falcon Works at Loughborough and which BR works?

11 Preserved No 13000 of 1952 was the prototype of which large TOPS class of diesel shunters?

12 Despite having three axles on each bogie, the Class 31s were not Co-Co locos. What was their wheel notation?

13 Which Lancashire manufacturer built the Class 20s from 1957 to 1966?

14 The Metrovick Co-Bos were initially used to double-head which prestigious London-Glasgow freight service in 1959, the forerunner of the 'Freightliner'?

15 Which route did the first batch of HSTs work on their introduction in service in 1976?

16 Class 59 Nos 59101-4 imported by ARC/Hanson Quarry Products were built by General Motors in London – but which London?

17 Enthusiasts have given the Class 60s the nicknames 'Doughnuts', 'Politicians' and 'Polos', all derived from the same aspect of their design – what is it?

18 The members of which class of BR diesel were nicknamed 'Growlers' and 'Syphons'?

19 The Class 56 locos were built by a Brush sub-contractor in which country?

20 The names *Scafell Pike* and *Scafell* were applied to diesel locos 32 years apart. The first was D1, but which class was the second?

Common names I

When the answers to the following clues are entered in the grid, their initial letters will spell out a word they all have in common.

1
2
3
4
5
6
7

1 'Tomb of the Unknown ___', in Westminster Abbey (7)
2 Capt Kirk's starship (10)
3 Shrewsbury manufacturer of steam lorries and railcars (8)
4 Magic charm, and an 1825 novel by Sir Walter Scott (8)
5 *The ___ Strikes Back*, 1980 'Star Wars' film (6)
6 ___ Street, London shopping street between Oxford Circus and Piccadilly Circus (6)
7 Person of high birth, a peer perhaps (8)

Number crunching 1

Across

1 Number given to Churchward 4-6-0 prototype *William Dean* of 1902 (3)
3 D___, 'Warship' *Ark Royal* (3)
5 Number of wheels on a 'Pacific' locomotive … (2)
6 … and its wheel arrangement (1-1-1)
7 Number of the preserved GNR 'Atlantic' *Henry Oakley* (3)
9 'Prairie' wheel arrangement (1-1-1)
11 First three digits on a 'Merchant Navy' numberplate (3)
13 TOPS class number of diesels in the former D55XX series (2)
14 BR number of preserved 'A2' *Blue Peter* (5)
17 1 in ___, gradient for the majority of the S&DJR line from Radstock to Evercreech over Masbury summit (2)
18 'Jinty' wheel arrangement (1-1-1)
19 'J___', class number of 18 across tanks Nos 68890-991, nicknamed 'Ardsley Tanks' (2)
20 ___A, BR shedcode for Inverness (Lochgorm) (2)
21 TOPS number of the electric locomotive named *Royal Sovereign* (5)
22 TOPS class number of the 'Western' diesel-hydraulics (2)
23 W___, number of the preserved Isle of Wight 'O2' *Calbourne* (2)
24 Number of preserved War Department 2-10-0 *Gordon* (3)
25 TOPS class number of diesel shunters in the former D3XXX series (2)
27 Number of BR Standard 4-6-0 *King Pellinore* (5)
30 TOPS class number of the 'Peaks' (2)

32 ___ *Squadron*, 'Battle of Britain' No 34078 (3)
34 HST, also known as IC ___ (3)
35 Number of the preserved LB&SCR 2 down loco *Gladstone* (3)
36 Number of the 1902 GNR 'large Atlantic' in the National Collection (3)
37 ___A, BR shedcode for Leeds (Holbeck) (2)
38 Wheel arrangement of the LNWR 'Super D' (1-1-1)
39 Number of the preserved Caledonian Railway 4-2-2 single of 1886 (3)

Down
 1 D___, preserved Class 22 across *Western Fusilier* (4)
 2 Wheel arrangement of No 35 across (1-1-1)
 3 LMS number of 'Duchess' 6 across *Coronation* (4)
 4 1 January ___, day that the 'Big Four' companies came into existence (4)
 5 Number of the preserved 'Jones Goods', Britain's first 4-6-0 loco (3)
 8 TOPS number of the preserved Type 4 D212 *Aureol* (5)
10 LMS number of the preserved *Royal Scot* (4)
12 'Deltic' TOPS class number (2)
14 BR number of 'V2' *St Peter's School York AD 627* (5)
15 TOPS number of the former D431 *Hood* (5)
16 TOPS number of the preserved former D7615 *Harlech Castle* (5)
20 *Mallard*'s BR number (5)
22 GWR 4-6-0 *Winchester Castle* (4)
26 ___A, BR shedcode for Bristol (Bath Road) (2)
28 Number of preserved GWR 4-4-0 *City of Truro* (4)
29 GWR 'County' 4-6-0 *County of Monmouth* (4)
31 LMS number of preserved 'Jubilee' *Kolhapur* (4)
33 D___, *Lusitania* (3)
34 Number of Britain's first 6 across, *The Great Bear* (3)

Out of town

Identify the names of the following railway locations, and you will see that they all
have something in common – but somewhere else…

 1 Maryport & Carlisle station between Carlisle and Wigston
 2 Midland junction NW of Settle Junction
 3 Terminus of an NER branch from Eryholme
 4 Town on the Avon at the end of the North Warwickshire line
 5 GER station in Yarmouth
 6 Midland Railway Centre station
 7 North British station in Glasgow, in the 1970s 'for King's Theatre'

Crossword No 7

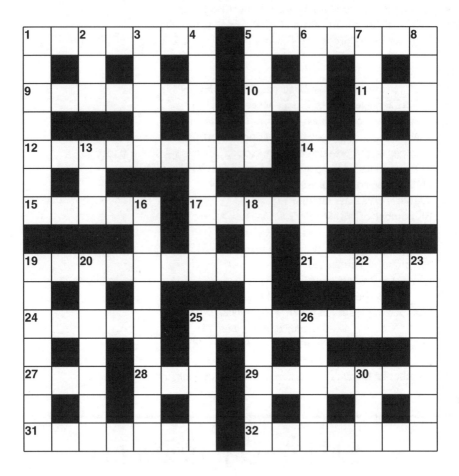

Across

1 *King* ___, preserved No 6024 (6,1)

5 Station on the Retford-Sheffield line (7)

9 ___ ___ & Somercotes, station on the GNR's Pinxton branch north of Nottingham (3,4)

10 Short-named GNR station south of 14 across (3)

11 '___ & Shove Behind', nickname for the Rhondda & Swansea Bay Railway (3)

12 'West Country' No 34028 (9)

14 GNR Lincolnshire junction between Grimsby and Boston (5)

15 Yarmouth ___ Town, GER seaside terminus (5)

17 Rotherfield & ___ ___, LB&SCR station between Groombridge and Polegate (4,5)

19 Preserved GWR 'Castle' No 4079 (9)

21 GWR telegraphic code-name for goods brake-vans (5)

24 The ___ Scouts, 6 down No 46128 (5)
25 Steam loco driver's control valve (9)
27 Fuel first used in Britain by the 1893 GER 2-4-0 *Petrolea* (3)
28 '2-___' and '4-___', BR Southern Region EMUs distinguished by their brake type (1,1,1)
29 North London Railway station north of Bow (3,4)
31 Tunnel between Bath and Bristol (7)
32 Great ___, 'A1' No 60157 (7)

Down
1 Fast non-stop train (7)
2 Severn & ___ & Severn Bridge Joint Railway (3)
3 They may be flat-bottom or bullhead (5)
4 'Patriot' No 45511 (4,2,3)
5 George ___, successor to Webb as CME of the LNWR, 1903-8 (5)
6 London Euston-Glasgow 1 down introduced in 1927 (5,4)
7 'A3' No 60083 (3,4)
8 ___ Grange, No 6868 (7)
13 Roderick ___, 'D11/2' No 62693 (3)
16 GER Walthamstow station that became Walthamstow Central in 1968 (3,6)
18 Shed 10F near Burnley, which lasted to the end of steam (4,5)
19 Station between Edinburgh and Glasgow on the former North British route (7)
20 ___ Hill, diesel depot name carried by HST power car No 43049 (7)
22 Controversial tilting train concept abandoned in the 1980s (1,1,1)
23 ___ Halt, GWR station between Banbury and Kingham (7)
25 ___ Hood, 'Britannia' No 70038 (5)
26 'A3' No 60067 (5)
30 Station east of Hastings (3)

The long and the short

The answer to 10 across is a station with a name of only three letters,
while we are all familiar with the LNWR station at
Llanfairpwllgwyngyllgogerychwyrndrobwllllantysiliogogogoch!
Loco nameplates also come in a variety of lengths…

1 Which loco works' internal system was operated by *Bee*, *Dot* and *Fly*, among others?
2 Which class of LNER engines included two examples named *The Snapper, The East Yorkshire Regiment, The Duke of York's Own* and *The Green Howard, Alexandra, Princess of Wales's Own Yorkshire Regiment*?
3 Named *H.L.I.* in 1927, the LMS 'Royal Scot' loco was given its full name in 1949. What did 'H.L.I.' stand for?
4 The shortest Class 47 name, carried by 47846, was originally carried by D1671 – what is it?
5 Which antelope provided the shortest nameplate for the LNER's 'B1' Class?

Down main 1: Southern

The answers to the following clues are all locations on the former Southern Railway system. When all the answers are in place, the letters in the two marked columns will spell out the starting point and destination of a principal down journey by the Southern.

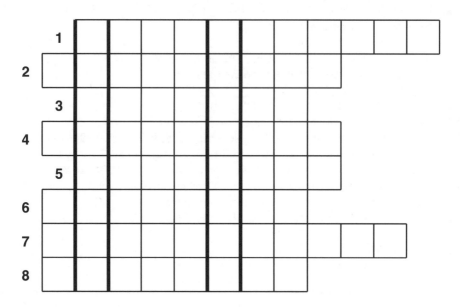

1 Station on the Hayes branch in south-east London (4,7)
2 Principal SR loco works, in Hampshire (9)
3 Terminus of a short branch up on to the Downs west of Brighton (3,4)
4 ___ & Littlestone-on-Sea, terminus of a short South Coast branch from Lydd (3,6)
5 Junction where the Midland & South Western Junction line met the SR main line west of Andover (3,5)
6 City that had SR stations known as Friary and Turnchapel (8)
7 Station between Coleford Junction and Okehampton (5,6)
8 Summit and last station before the terminus of the Ilfracombe branch (8)

The Big Four: Southern Railway

1   What was unique about the 1934 all-Pullman train the 'Brighton Belle'?

2   The Southern had more London termini than any other of the 'Big Four' – how many, and which were they?

3   What geographical features provided the names applied by the Southern in 1924 to the LB&SCR 'Atlantics'?

4   The independent Colonel Stephens-built North Devon & Cornwall Junction Light Railway was worked by the SR from its opening in 1925, and linked Torrington to which SR junction station?

5   Which narrow-gauge railway was closed by the Southern in September 1935?

6   The LSWR established a works at Exmouth Junction in 1913 and the Southern was well-known for making extensive use of its product – what was the product?

7   In 1939 the Southern opened a new line from Motspur Park Junction, SW London, originally intended to reach Leatherhead, but only completed as far as which 'North' and 'South' stations?

8   The Southern opened its new Exeter Central station in 1933. What was the original LSWR name for the station?

9   '6-PAN' six-car EMU sets were built in 1935 for the newly electrified services to Eastbourne and Hastings. What feature of the trains was indicated by the 'PAN'?

10 Which nautically named 1926 locomotive was described by SR publicity as 'the most powerful British locomotive', outstripping the GWR 'Castles' and early LNER 'Pacifics'?

11 What was the class name of the most powerful 4-4-0 locomotives in Britain, introduced by the Southern in 1930?

12 To which Chief Mechanical Engineer was O. V. S. Bulleid Assistant when he was appointed to the CME's job on the Southern?

13 Bulleid adopted a French-style numbering system for his new 'Pacifics'. *Channel Packet* was No 21C1, the last '1' indicating its number within the class, and the first '2' and '1' indicating the number of leading and trailing axles respectively. What did the letter 'C' indicate?

14 The Southern Railway cross-Channel steamer *Canterbury* was designated exclusively for the use of passengers from which train?

15 The impetus for the SR's provision of freight and passenger cross-Channel services was Parliamentary rejection of which 1930 proposal?

16 To this day a road in the New Docks area of Southampton is named after the SR General Manager who conceived the improvement plans in the 1920s-'30s. Who was he?

17 On 27 May 1936 No 852 *Sir Walter Raleigh* hauled an Ocean Liner Special to Southampton for the maiden voyage of which famous liner?

18 For which Southern hump and marshalling yard did Urie build four 4-8-0T shunting locos of the 'H16' Class?

19 Which famous 1926 SR train included separate carriages for Salisbury, Sidmouth, Exmouth, Plymouth, Padstow, Bude and Ilfracombe?

20 Which weight-saving aspect of SR 'Pacifics' was a Bulleid-Firth-Brown development, also known as 'Boxpok'?

Fit the Bill

1 The pioneering *Puffing Billy* of 1813 took its name from its designer. Who was he?

2 A pioneering locomotive preservationist Bill was honoured when Class 33 No 33109 was named after him. What was his rank and name as given on the nameplate?

3 The first of the GWR 'Saint' Class loco was named *William Dean* by that gentleman's successor as GWR Loco Superintendent – who was he?

4 Two Williams were commemorated on 'Britannia' nameplates – who were they?

5 In 1941, which William was replaced by *Tagalie*, but himself replaced *Great Snipe*?

Hoover hunt!

The original names of all 50 Class 50 locos are hidden in this grid of letters.
The words may read backwards, forwards, up, down, or diagonally, but always in a
straight line and never skipping letters. Not all the letters in the grid are used, while
some are used more than once.

```
V M A H R A B O B U L W A R K T D
I H I P O T E M E R A I R E S P O
C A E M R O N R E T E X E P U Z O
T H G U O N D A E R D P Z U L C W
O E N I D N G R I G E E U L T E G
R R E R N L A A A L I N N S N N N
I C V T E C W R C U A T O E E T I
O U E S Y L O E C H G V S W C U L
U L R D U Y B U T H I N N R N R L
S E E I A O A A R I S L A C I I O
S S O L N U I M C T P M L V V O C
A S O B B V N R G A I S P E T N O
R A E I E A I T T L L R E S O U
K J N L D N D N L S O P B A E I R
R A E I R Y B I C E U R M W W T A
O X P O I A E O M I S L I I O U G
Y L T N L S E A W R B S L O H L E
A S U O I R U F D A O L M I U O O
L S N O N F E C N A I F E D R S U
I D E A Y I N D O M I T A B L E S
S W I F T S U R E O F N E D T R A
T H U N D E R E R O R E U Q N O C
```

Crossword No 8

Across

4 Mountain ___, station on GWR and Taff Vales lines south of Aberdare (3)

8 *City of ___*, No 46240 (8)

9 *King ___*, No 30453 (6)

10 1961 experimental Brush diesel loco No D0280 (6)

11 'Patriot' No 45539 (1,1,6)

13 Aston ___, station on the GWR's Watlington branch (6)

14 Nickname for the GNR's first 0-8-0s, from the length of their boilers (4,4)

15 NBR station on the coast between Thornton Junction and St Andrews (4)

16 Intermediate station on the LSWR's Midhurst branch (6)

18 ___ Court, Piccadilly and District Line station east of Hammersmith (6)

21 North Wales coast line station (4)

22 Tunnel and former station on the Yeovil-Weymouth line (8)

24 GCR station between Barnetby and Frodingham (6)
26 Piccadilly Line station east of Hounslow (8)
29 East ___ and West ___, signal boxes west of Lincoln Central station (6)
30 *St ___*, 'A3' No 60073 (6)
31 Enthusiasts' excursion (8)
32 ___ and Mite, rivers followed by the narrow-gauge line from Ravenglass to Boot (3)

Down

1 'Jubilee' No 45635 (6)
2 ___ *Taylors*, 'Schools' No 30910 (8)
3 Airport served by a spur from the main Cambridge line (8)
4 Green ___, Lancaster's MR station (4)
5 ___ *Hall*, 'Modified Hall' No 7907 (4)
6 Baker, Broad or Liverpool in London, eg (6)
7 *Flying ___*, 'Britannia' No 70018 (8)
12 *Glen ___*, 'D34' No 62474 (4)
13 ___ & Camber Railway (3)
14 ___ Railway Act, 1896, allowing railways of a cheaper and simpler construction (5)
17 North Yorkshire Moors Railway station (8)
18 'Castle' No 5073, and 'A3' No 60087 (8)
19 Name carried by Class 47 No 47642 and 47766 (8)
20 Sir ___ Fay, GCR General Manager (3)
21 *Princess Margaret ___*, preserved LMS 'Pacific' (4)
23 *Auld ___*, 'A1' No 60160 (6)
25 Leamington Spa ___, the LNWR's station in the town (6)
27 Stewarts ___, South London loco depot (4)
28 Home of the National Railway Museum (4)

Preserved stations

The answer to 17 down is an intermediate station on the North Yorkshire Moors Railway. Which preserved lines feature the following stations?

1 Market Bosworth

2 Quorn & Woodhouse

3 Coleslogget Halt

4 Damems

5 Summerseat

6 Merryfield Lane

7 Orton Mere

8 Highley

9 Norden

10 Glyndyfrdwy

Crossword No 9

Across

1 and 5 across Tunnel and station between 29 across Hill and Norwood Junction (7,6)

9 Station on the GWR's Launceston branch (7)

10 BR 'EM2' No 27005 (7)

11 Single intermediate station on the 34 across branch (3)

12 'Britannia' No 70031 (5)

13 'Stop and ___ train', meaning of the telegraph bell code of 7 bells consecutively (7)

14 Company formed in 1854 from the York, Newcastle & Berwick, York & North Midland, Leeds Northern, and Malton & Driffield (1,1,1)

15 Former Berkshire county town with GWR and LSWR stations (7)

17 ___ Park, station on the GER's 5 across Gates branch in North London (4)

21 Perry ___ and Great ___, former LNWR stations in north Birmingham (4)

24 '___ City', former express between Glasgow Buchanan Street and Aberdeen (7)

27 See 18 down

28 Foss ___ Junction, northern end of the Derwent Valley Railway in York (7)

29 ___ Hill, South London station with lines radiating to Balham, Streatham and 1 and 5 across (5)

30 Term used to describe a signal in the 'clear' position (3)

31 Self-advertising (though not always geographically accurate) word appended to stations in Leicester, Loughborough and Rugby (7)

32 Former Settle & Carlisle station south of Appleby (7)

33 ___ Road, Waverley Route station south of Riccarton Junction (6)

34 Terminus of a Midland Railway branch from the main line at Coaley Junction (7)

Down

1 *Colonel Bill* ___ *CBE TD*, name formerly carried by Class 90 No 90020 (8)

2 Former platform at King's Cross for the southbound Widened Lines (4,4)

3 Large marshalling yard in the Erewash Valley north of Trent (5)

4 Location of the LB&SCR's carriage works, closed in the 1960s (7)

5 'A1' No 60133 (7)

6 Station on the M&GNR's Norwich branch (7)

7 ___ Railway, incorporated in 1858 to carry slate to the Cambrian line at Machynlleth, closed in 1948 (6)

8 Sir Vincent ___, CME of the 14 across, 1910-22 (5)

16 Railwaymen's trade union that became the RMT in 1990 (1,1,1)

18 and 27 across '___ ___', name carried by Class 31 No 31455 (3,3)

19 ___ ___ Broadway, station on the Midland Main Line in north London (4,4)

20 Type of establishment served by the LSWR's Brookwood Necropolis station between 1854 and 1941 (8)

22 Station in north Liverpool where Class 86 No 86428 was a winner in 1981! (7)

23 Class 47 No 47769 (7)

24 Colin T. ___, 'New Wave' railway photographer of the 1965 album *Decline of Steam* (7)

25 ___ *Grove*, preserved LB&SCR 'E4' No 473 (5)

26 Name carried by at least 12 different locos, from a Liverpool & Manchester 2-2-0 of 1830 to Class 86 electric No 86218 (6)

29 River crossed by Brunel's Royal Albert Bridge (5)

Guessed houses

Can you match up the following railway-owned hotels with their locations?

1	Adelphi	Brighton	5	Terminus	Sheffield
2	Grosvenor	Fleetwood	6	Tregenna Castle	Stratford-upon Avon
3	North Euston	Liverpool			
4	Royal Victoria	London	7	Welcombe	St Ives

Loose-coupled I

Can you identify the quirky or cryptic links between the following groups?

1 What is the questionable link between the penultimate station on the Hertford East branch, a Scottish steam engine pioneer, and 'Jubilee' No 45644?

2 Which name is linked with Burton, Chalfont and Road in station names?

3 What is the railway connection between the world's largest ocean, a former Indian emperor or business magnate, and an American treeless, grass-covered plain?

4 What is the elevated connection between a return ticket at a cheap rate if booked seven days in advance, introduced in 1990, a tunnel between Rochdale and Todmorden, and D1, eg?

5 What is the connection between a *Brown* 'A3', the North British's Glasgow Street, No 6000 and his companions, and an abbreviated Southern holiday express?

6 What is the connection between the junction for the Littlehampton branch, a south-of-the-river Victoria Line station, and a GWR broad gauge class of 4-2-2s that replaced the 'Iron Dukes', and why were they a threat to railways?

7 What word is spelled by knighted 'King Arthur' No 30450, the terminus of a short GER branch from Mellis, and the river crossed by a 19-arch viaduct at Cefn, near Chirk?

8 Who are a signalman, colloquially speaking, a loco-hauled First Class Pullman Kitchen Car, and *Blue* No 60532, and what is their connection with the fictitious Northern & Southern Railway?

9 What is the clean connection between the Falcon Works at Loughborough, the western extremity of the Stratford-upon-Avon & Midland Junction Railway, and a Class 50 nickname?

10 What word is common to the BR computerised operating system introduced in the 1970s, a type of GWR carriage introduced in the 1908-20 period, and King's Cross loco depot?

11 Why might the terminus of a steep branch from Brighton, 'Patriot' No 45539 and the Waterloo & City line need be excavated?

12 What is the capital connection between a Suffolk village and seat of the Duke of Grafton, a battle of 1815, and the Queen of England, 1837-1901?

13 What is the musical connection between the GER's intensive Liverpool Street suburban services of the 1920s, Ross & Co's safety valves, and a Merseyside Ferry station between Hooton and Birkenhead?

14 What are Nos 60106 and 70018 and Battledown Junction all doing?

15 What comical first name might be shared by the inventor of the 'lock and block' signalling system, a station on the GNR's Shipley branch, and an LMS West Coast seaside resort with a Promenade station?

16 What is the connection between a class of GWR 2-4-0 tanks introduced in 1869, the Home Counties commuter belt served by trains from Baker Street, and Manchester's rapid transit system?

17 What is the connection between an L&YR 0-4-0T dock loco, a GWR 4-4-0 of the '33XX' Class, and an LSWR Drummond 'T9' 4-4-0?

18 What is the connection between the LNER 'B17s', 'A1' No 60140, and GWR No 4082?

19 What is the connection between 'Jubilee' No 45659, Thomas's GWR pannier tank companion, and the world's fastest steam locomotive?

20 What is the connection between preserved Class 50 No 50017, the GWR's principal London steam shed, and *The Railway Children* station on the Keighley & Worth Valley Railway?

In short

In the world of railways, for what do the following initials stand?

1 ARPS	**8** GUV	**15** SLS
2 ASLEF	**9** HMRS	**16** SLOA
3 AWS	**10** LUL	**17** TMD
4 BRCW	**11** NCL	**18** TOPS
5 BTC	**12** PWS	**19** VSOE
6 DART	**13** RCH	**20** WTT
7 DVT	**14** ROD	

Crossword No 10

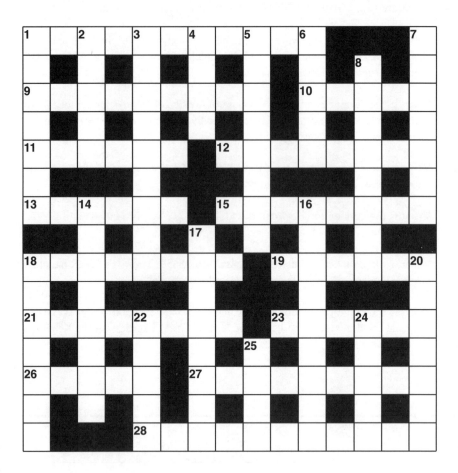

Across

1 Preserved GWR 4-6-0 No 7827 (6,5)

9 City with a Shrub Hill station (9)

10 ___ cocks, necessary to remove condensed steam from steam loco cylinders (5)

11 *The* ___, 'Royal Scot' No 46154 (6)

12 Place name preceding Kings and Mackrell on the GWR (8)

13 ___ *Hall*, preserved GWR 4-6-0 No 4942 (6)

15 'West Country' No 34021 (8)

18 ___ *Hall*, No 5926 (8)

19 *Sun* ___, 'A2/3' No 60515 (6)

21 ___ & Four Marks, Mid-Hants Railway station (8)

23 GER junction for the Eye branch (6)

26 ___ Street, principal Metropolitan Railway station (5)

27 'Lord Nelson' No 30860 (4,5)
28 GWR 4-6-0 No 4925 (7,4)

Down
1 Station between Newark and Nottingham (7)
2 Girl's name, and a First Class Pullman EMU Kitchen Car (5)
3 ___ Reith Gray, 'B1' No 61242 (9)
4 River ___, Ravenglass & Eskdale Railway 2-8-2 (4)
5 Kent & East Sussex Railway station (8)
6 Former Taff Vale station north of Cardiff (5)
7 Seaside town and southern terminus of the Isle of Wight Railway (7)
8 Intermediate station on the NBR's Aberfoyle branch (8)
14 GWR broad gauge loco of 1847, 'Britannia' No 70014, and Class 87 No 87017 (4,4)
16 ___ Corner, race-goers' terminus of a branch from Smitham (9)
17 Pioneering trainspotters' publisher (3,5)
18 'B1' No 61020 (7)
20 ___ Hill, station on the GNR's Alexandra Palace branch in North London (7)
22 Intermediate station between Newton Abbot and Paignton (5)
24 Cleator & Workington Junction Railway terminus station (5)
25 Brick ___, structure in a steam loco firebox (4)

Same name, different loco

Clue 14 down referred to a famous name carried by various locomotives from the 1840s to the 1970s. Here are some more examples.

1 The name of which Rainhill Trials competitor of 1829 has also appeared on three LNWR engines, a 'Royal Scot', a 'Jubilee' and a Class 86 electric?

2 Of the nine planets in the Solar System, two have had 20 locos named after them, from a Liverpool & Manchester Railway 2-2-0 of 1830 to a preserved Class 25. Which two are they – and which has never been used?

3 King George V is a famous preserved GWR locomotive, but which company had given one of its 4-4-0s the same name 16 years earlier?

4 Most of the names of D1 to D10 re-appeared some 30 years later on which other class of diesel-electrics?

5 The name of which preserved GWR 'Castle' 4-6-0 has also appeared on a Class 37 and a Class 47 diesel-electric?

Crossword No 11

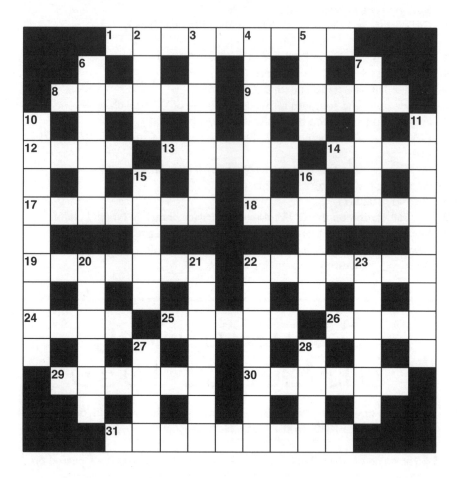

Across

1 ___ & Carlisle Railway, at 69 miles the largest construction contract ever placed on its authorisation in 1844 (9)

8 Nickname for a GCR Robinson 0-6-0, the sharp bark of its exhaust like a gun of the same name used in the South African War (3,3)

9 LNWR's principal London terminus (6)

12 Moses ___, station south of 6 down on the Manchester line (4)

13 See 7 down

14 **and 27 down** Liverpool steam shed, 8A (4,4)

17 'Battle of Britain' No 34070 (7)

18 ___ Central, ___ Downs and ___ Wick, North London/Great Eastern line stations (7)

19 Fort ___, last intermediate station on the Gourock branch (7)

22 Location of the North of England Open Air Museum (7)

24 ___ Viaduct, on the Brighton line south of Balcombe (4)

25 Staffordshire location of a serious 6 January 1968 accident when a train struck a transformer lorry on a half-barrier level crossing (5)

26 and 3 down BR Standard 'Pacific' No 72001 (4,7)

29 Waverley Route station just south of Falahill summit (6)

30 ___ *Hall*, No 6913 (6)

31 Former station at the top of the Lickey Incline (9)

Down

2 'Over the ___', enginemen's nickname for the hilly Alton-Alresford line, among others (4)

3 See 26 across

4 G&SWR terminus in Glasgow (2,5)

5 and 21 down ___ ___ *Company*, 'Merchant Navy' No 35024 (4,7)

6 ___ Street station, Bury, headquarters of the East Lancashire Railway (6)

7 and 13 across Former Pullman express from London to Folkestone/Dover for Paris (6,5)

10 'Jubilee' No 45693 (9)

11 'Peak' D8 (9)

15 Come to halt on an incline, short of steam, perhaps (5)

16 ___ *Swell*, 'A2/3' No 60517 (5)

20 LSWR Meon Valley line station south of Alton (6)

21 See 5 down

22 'A3' No 60088 (4,3)

23 Type of platform with lines at both faces (6)

27 See 14 across

28 Cricketers' Northern Line station (4)

Name-calling 1

A steam loco nickname is referred to in 8 across. Which railway companies introduced the steam locos that were given the following nicknames?

1 Cauliflowers
2 Combine Harvesters
3 Directors
4 Flying Pigs
5 Greyhounds
6 Humpty Dumpties
7 Ragtimers
8 Spam Cans
9 Spinners
10 Woolworths

Titled trains

1   What is thought to be the first name officially given to a train service, by the Chester & Holyhead Railway in 1848?

2   'Three Guineas for a Name for a Train! An Interesting and Easy Competition' announced *The Railway Magazine* in July 1904. Which named train was the result?

3   The LMS's misnamed 'Midday Scot' actually left Euston at which time?

4   What word followed 'Hull', 'Cleveland' and 'Bradford' on BR expresses of the 1970s and early 1980s?

5   What word followed 'Cornish', 'Devon' and 'Wessex' on BR expresses of the 1980s?

6   With reference to the name 'Freightliner', what nickname was applied to a BR container train carrying household refuse?

7   Which capitals were united by the 1956-65 service the 'Capitals United Express'?

8   The East Coast 'Capitals Limited' was renamed in 1953 to commemorate an event of that year. What was its new name?

9   What feature of the countryside around Bournemouth gave its name to a famous express linking the resort with Manchester?

10   Which word followed 'Bournemouth', 'Thanet', 'Devon' and 'Kentish' on various express services between 1931 and 1967?

11   The last Pullman cars built in Great Britain were for a named service introduced in 1966 between London and which city?

12   Which London-Sheffield express departed from Marylebone on its introduction in 1947, King's Cross (as a Pullman train) from 1958, and St Pancras from 1968?

13   What did the 'Bristol Pullman' (from 1960) and the 'South Wales Pullman' (after 1961) have in common?

14   Which of the following river names has not appeared in the title of a named train: Clyde, Thames, Trent, Tyne?

15   What was the connection between Mary, daughter of King James V of Scotland, and an East Coast Main Line Pullman train?

16 What new wordless design of headboard was carried by 'Deltics' on the 'Flying Scotsman' from 1964?

17 Which new express train was introduced on the GWR main line to celebrate the company's centenary in 1935?

18 What is the literary connection between the 'Waverley', 'Talisman' and 'Heart of Midlothian' express services?

19 Which East Coast port was used by the GER's 'Continental Express' and its successor, the LNER's 'Hook Continental'?

20 Which two cities were linked by the Western Region's 'Inter-City Express' in 1950?

In shape

Which of the pictured shapes would you associate with each of the clues?

1 Forster, in Bradford

2 Ambergate station, eg

3 Bayswater, Barbican and Blackfriars, eg

4 Northern Line, south of Kennington

5 *Knight of the Garter*, eg

6 Two tracks crossing diagonally

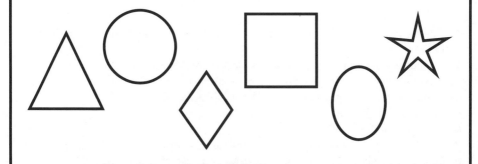

Tri-composite

When all the words are in place, take the letters in the three tinted squares
in each answer and drop them, in the same order, into the lower grid. There, reading
across, they will spell out a railway-themed remark that film legend Orson Welles made
when told he would be given artistic freedom by RKO, the studio where he made
Citizen Kane. Thick lines in the lower grid indicate word-breaks,
and words run on from one line to the next.

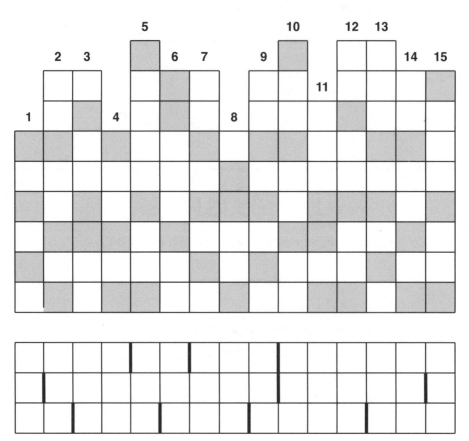

1   Town whose Riverside station is at the southern end of the South Devon Railway
    (6)
2   Composer whose name is carried by electric loco No 92007 (8)
3   Railway company that built the Kyle of Lochalsh line (8)
4   Tunnel 4⅓ miles long built by the GWR in 1873-86 (6)
5   Term used by BR from 1966 for its fast trunk services (9)
6   'B1' No 61039 (8)
7   ___ & City line, London, known affectionately by commuters as 'The Drain' (8)
8   East Coast port and resort that had Town and West Cliff stations (6)

9   Edward ___, Loco Superintendent of the NER, 1854-82 (8)
10 Composer whose name is carried by electric loco No 92003 (9)
11 Locomotive with a 2-6-2 wheel arrangement (7)
12 Steam loco driver's control lever (9)
13 Manchester steam shed that was coded 9A (9)
14 ___ Castle, GWR 4-6-0 No 5006 (8)
15 NER seaside station, the first north of answer 8 West Cliff (8)

Railways on screen

1   Which UK preserved line was used for scenes in the James Bond films *Octopussy* and *Goldeneye?*

2   The 1970 film of *The Railway Children* was shot on the Keighley & Worth Valley Railway, but which preserved line was used for the 2000 Carlton TV adaptation?

3   Which WCML station was famously used as the location for David Lean's 1945 classic *Brief Encounter?*

4   Which famous preserved 1838 locomotive played *The Titfield Thunderbolt* in 1952?

5   The action of the classic 1955 Ealing comedy *The Ladykillers* took place around the tunnels outside which London terminus?

6   Crossing Glenfinnan Viaduct, *Harry Potter's* 'Hogwarts Express' was followed by which make of car?

7   Which red-liveried preserved former GWR locomotive hauled the train?

8   On which famous bridge does Richard Hannay (Robert Donat) leave his train in the 1935 Hitchcock thriller *The Thirty-Nine Steps?*

9   That bridge was unavailable for the 1978 remake starring Robert Powell, so a well-known bridge on a preserved line was used instead – which?

10 Cliddesden station, on the Alton-Basingstoke line, doubled for which Irish station in the Will Hay comedy *Oh! Mr Porter* in 1937?

11 The previous year a famous railway documentary film featured a poem by W. H. Auden. The second line is 'Bringing the cheque and the postal order' – what is the first line?

12 In 1967 the Rugby-Market Harborough line near Theddingworth was used to make a feature film dramatising a famous event on the WCML four years earlier – which?

13 For the 1978 film *The First Great Train Robbery* starring Sean Connery, London's Victoria station was recreated at Heuston station – in which city?

14 Which Severn Valley Railway station became 'Hatley' for the BBC sitcom *Oh, Dr Beeching*?

15 The 1923 stage play *The Ghost Train* was adapted for TV and film in 1925, 1927, 1931, 1937 and 1941, but which member of the cast of TV's *Dad's Army* wrote the original?

16 Which London terminus was invaded by screaming fans for the opening of the Beatles' film *A Hard Day's Night* in 1964?

17 Which then recently closed system in Hampshire was used for location filming for *The Great St Trinian's Train Robbery* in 1966?

18 Heavily disguised 'Black Five' No 44871 was used in a derailment scene in the 1969 film *The Virgin Soldiers*, and was scrapped on site afterwards, despite having taken part in a famous railway event of the previous year – which?

19 The 1958-62 TV series Railway Roundabout was made and presented by John Adams and which late railway author?

20 One of the best-loved of the British Transport Films, made in 1955, told the story of a snowdrift at which Pennine location?

Flower power

From each of the following clues the name of a plant or flower is missing. Can you identify them all?

1 ____ Railway, based at Sheffield Park
2 ____ Line, based at Isfield station
3 ____ Grove, shed 10F
4 ____ Hill, tunnels and junctions outside Euston
5 *Knight of the ____*, GWR 'Star'
6 ____ Hill, Manchester-Wigan
7 ____ Bourton, Bristol-Bridgwater
8 ____bridge, Totnes-Plymouth
9 ____ Street, Uxbridge GWR
10 'Jersey ____', GCR 'Atlantic' nickname

Capital quest

The names of the 30 stations on London's underground system listed below are hidden in this grid of letters. The words may read backwards, forwards, up, down, or diagonally, but always in a straight line and never skipping letters.
Not all the letters in the grid are used, while some are used more than once.

O	T	H	B	I	P	P	I	M	L	I	C	O	B	S
P	X	A	U	W	I	I	E	T	A	G	R	O	O	M
Z	N	F	S	A	C	Z	N	R	L	E	W	A	R	I
K	S	S	O	R	C	S	G	N	I	K	S	C	O	L
N	N	E	D	R	A	G	T	N	E	V	O	C	U	E
I	O	M	S	E	D	I	N	E	I	R	A	P	G	E
G	I	N	L	N	I	C	R	I	M	P	L	L	H	N
H	E	T	O	S	L	D	I	F	K	P	P	B	E	D
T	A	E	A	T	L	Y	Y	R	K	R	L	A	W	C
S	I	E	N	R	Y	I	A	L	C	C	A	E	W	H
B	R	R	E	E	C	E	K	W	A	U	A	B	L	C
R	O	T	S	E	I	H	L	I	S	N	S	L	L	Y
I	T	S	Q	T	R	A	W	E	L	N	E	D	B	W
D	C	D	U	A	C	M	S	A	G	B	E	S	O	D
G	I	N	A	N	U	F	V	R	Y	N	U	E	R	L
E	V	O	R	G	S	O	N	R	A	I	A	R	U	A
D	A	B	E	T	H	N	A	L	G	R	E	E	N	Q

ALDWYCH
ANGEL
ARCHWAY
ARNOS GROVE
ARSENAL
BANK
BARKING
BETHNAL GREEN
BLACKFRIARS
BOND STREET

BOROUGH
COVENT GARDEN
KILBURN
KINGS CROSS
KNIGHTSBRIDGE
LEYTON
MILE END
MOORGATE
OVAL
OXFORD CIRCUS

PERIVALE
PICCADILLY CIRCUS
PIMLICO
PINNER
QUEENSWAY
SLOANE SQUARE
TEMPLE
VICTORIA
WAPPING
WARREN STREET

Down main 2: LNER

The answers to the following clues are all locations on the former LNER system. When all the answers are in place, the letters in the two marked columns will spell out the starting point and destination of a down journey on the East Coast Main Line.

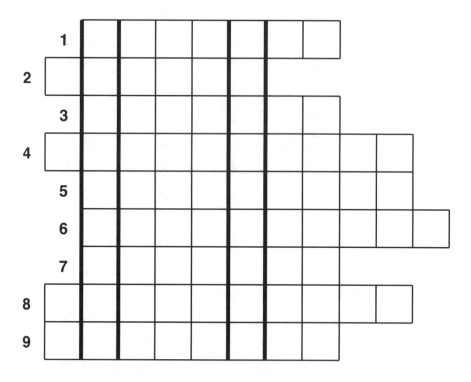

1 Station at the south end of the Forth Bridge (6)
2 Castle ___, station on the York-Malton line serving a famous stately home (6)
3 City with LNER stations at Thorpe and Victoria (7)
4 ECML station between Morpeth and Alnmouth (10)
5 Terminus of a seaside branch ... (9)
6 ... from this junction on the Ipswich-Lowestoft line (10)
7 West Highland line station north of Crianlarich (7)
8 ECML steam shed north of Peterborough station (3,7)
9 ECML station, junction for the Nottingham and Lincoln lines (8)

The Big Four: LNER

1 The LNER's motto on its coat of arms was 'Forward', borrowed from which of its constituent companies?

2 The first chairman of the LNER was the father of, and had the same name as, Margaret Thatcher's Home Secretary of 1979-83. Who was he?

3 The company's chief general manager was the great-great-grandson of a famous English potter – what was his name?

4 Which artist, who designed the type-face adopted by the LNER for all its printed matter, painted a headboard for the 'Flying Scotsman', his fee including a footplate ride?

5 What was the wheel arrangement of Gresley's high-pressure compound 'Hush Hush' locomotive of 1929?

6 Which class of Gresley locomotives carried cast brass foxes on the nameplates?

7 What was the name of the large marshalling yard built by the LNER in Cambridgeshire between 1925 and 1933?

8 What was the name of the 7-day holiday 'cruise train' operated by the LNER each June from 1933 to 1939, accommodating 60 holidaymakers?

9 What was unusual about the running-gear of Gresley's carriage sets for the 'Silver Jubilee' and 'Coronation' trains?

10 What feature of Gresley's streamlined 'Pacifics' was nicknamed the 'cod's mouth'?

11 What famous event brought crowds to King's Cross station on 1 May 1928?

12 The name of former NBR No 9903 was changed so that it could be carried by the LNER's new 1934 'P2' 2-8-2 loco No 2001, which kept it when converted to an 'A2/2' 'Pacific' in 1944. What was the name?

13 What name was given to the Pullman train that ran from King's Cross to Edinburgh and Glasgow, introduced in 1927?

14 The LNER had the majority interest in the Forth Bridge, three of the original four contributing companies being LNER constituents, the NBR, NER and GNR. Which was the fourth company?

15 Why did LNER loco No 6701 run in the Netherlands between 1947 and 1952?

16 On the 10.10am King's Cross-Leeds service between 1935 and 1939 passengers could pay an additional shilling and use a converted bogie brake-van – for what purpose?

17 What was the derivation of the names given to LNER Sentinel steam railcars such as *Trafalgar*, *British Queen*, *Rising Sun* and *Bang Up*?

18 No 4472 *Flying Scotsman* was exhibited at the British Empire Exhibition in 1925, in which newly built sports and exhibition complex?

19 The huge LNER Beyer Garratt 2-8-0+0-8-2 loco No 2395 was built to bank trains up which incline, later being transferred to the Lickey?

20 On 26 November 1937 the 100th 'Pacific' completed at Doncaster was named at Marylebone station. Apparently a railway enthusiast had suggested what its name should be – now preserved, what was it?

London A to Z

Can you identify these London Underground stations from their constituent letters, given in alphabetical order?

1   C C D F I O O R R S U X (6,6)

2   A A D D E E G O R R W (7,4)

3   A C E L O R R S T U (5,5)

4   A B E E E K R R S T T (5,6)

5   A C D E M N N O T W (6,4)

6   A E G G H I I L L N N O T T T (6,4,4)

7   A C E E E E I L Q R R S S T U (9,5)

8   A C D E E G N N O R T V (6,6)

9   B D E E H H H P R S S S U (9,4)

10 A C C C C D I I I L L P R S U Y (10,6)

Mind the gap!

Simply identify the missing word in each personal name, place name or locomotive name. A few additional clues are given.

Across

2 Newton ___ (5)
6 Cross ___ (GWR, South Wales) (4)
7 Lancaster 28 across ___ (4)
8 ___ *Hinchcliffe* (5)
11 ___ *Look East* (1,1,1)
13 ___ Allan (3)
15 Clipston & ___ (LNWR, Northants) (7)
16 Glasgow, Paisley, Kilmarnock & ___ Railway (1837) (3)
17 ___ *Valley* (3)
18 Double ___ (eg *Merddin Emrys*) (7)
19 *Sir Frank* ___ (3)
21 ___ *Castle OBE* (3)
23 St Philip's ___ (5)
26 *Princess Margaret* ___ (4)
27 ___ Park (Hayes branch) (4)
28 Bath ___ Park (5)

Down

1 Francis W. ___ (LNWR) (4)
2 Mountain ___ (3)
3 Potters ___ (3)
4 ___ Bridge (3)
5 *Carn* ___ *Castle* (4)
9 *Holland-___ Line* (7)
10 Robert A. ___ (7)
11 ___ *Athol* (5)
12 ___ Castle (Swanage Railway) (5)
13 ___ City (5)
14 ___ Bridge (Lakeside & Haverthwaite) (5)
20 Windsor & ___ Riverside (4)
22 ___ *Glendower* (4)
23 ___ *Merrilies* (3)
24 Peckham ___ (3)
25 Felin ___ (LNWR Bethesda branch) (3)

Crossword No 12

Across

7 Birmingham's principal station (3,6)

8 *Great* ___, preserved 'Peak' D4 (5)

10 Lower ___, station on the Enfield Town/Cheshunt line in North London (8)

11 *Sir* ___, preserved SR 'King Arthur' No 777 (6)

12 '___ Bogies', nickname given to a class of David Jones Highland Railway 4-4-0s (4)

13 American term for a loco driver (8)

15 and 9 down Lead device protecting a steam loco's firebox crown from overheating (7,4)

17 'Castle' No 5018 (2,5)

20 Seaside resort claimed by the Great Northern to be 'So Bracing!' (8)

22 *Sir Meleaus de* ___, SR 'King Arthur' No 30800 ... (4)

25 ... and a name on the same theme carried by BR Standard No 73114 (6)

26 Preserved Class 50 No 50050 (8)

27 '___ Diversion', 14-mile line between Temple Hirst and Colton, opened in 1983 (5)

28 Preserved No 70000 (9)

Down

1 City with Central, City and Wellington stations (5)

2 Veteran railway book author who died in 1994 (1,1,4)

3 ___ *Manor*, No 7815 (8)

4 'Jubilee' Nos 5690, preserved, ... (7)

5 ... and 45569, scrapped! (8)

6 Preserved 'A2' No 60532 (4,5)

9 See 15 across

14 *Western* ___, No D1030 (9)

16 Station on the GNR's Leicester Belgrave Road branch (8)

18 Cambrian station south of Three Cocks, and ___ *Hall*, No 4974 (8)

19 Kent station served by Eurostar trains (7)

21 ___ Valley Junction, where the NER Kirkby Stephen line left the LNWR main line south of Penrith (4)

23 Station on the St Ives branch (6)

24 Station on the Oxford-Bicester line (5)

All Saints

St Ives (23 down) and St Erth form the two ends of a Cornish branch line. From the following clues, can you identify seven further saints?

1 The principal Caledonian Railway works in Glasgow

2 Hertfordshire city that had London Rd, City and Abbey stations

3 Station on the Isle of Wight's Bembridge branch and the Swansea & Mumbles Railway as well as a town with Central and Shaw Street stations

4 GWR 'Saint' No 2925, which became 'Hall' prototype No 4900

5 'Deltic' D9001

6 G&SWR terminus in Glasgow

7 'A1' No 60145, Class 47 47703 and Class 86 86425

Crossword No 13

Across

1 and 4 ECML location of an 1876 accident in falling snow that led the GNR to adopt somersault signals (6,6)

9 Initials of the company that began life as the London & Southampton in 1834 (1,1,1,1)

10 'B1' No 61001 (5)

11 *Princess* ___, No 46202, the recently converted 'Turbomotive' wrecked in the Harrow & Wealdstone crash of 1952 (4)

12 Term applied to a locomotive of 2-8-2 wheel arrangement (6)

13 'Warship' D853 (8)

14 ___ Lake Railway, Snowdonia narrow-gauge line (9)

16 and 17 'Lord Nelson' No 30857 (4,4)

18 Thurnby & ___, station on the GNR's Leicester Belgrave Road branch (9)

22 Kyle of Lochalsh line station (8)
23 *Dick* ___, 'A3' No 60080 (6)
25 Arrangement whereby a signal arm can be worked from two signal boxes, only showing clear when both signalmen have pulled off (4)
26 Common name for subsidiary posts/arms on a bracket signal (5)
27 Term applied to the line generally running away from London or other major centre (4)
28 Station on the GWR's Bala-Blaenau Ffestiniog branch (6)
29 ___ *Grange*, No 6824 (6)

Down
1 Settle & Carlisle line summit (3,4)
2 'Jubilee' No 45580 (5)
3 'West Country' No 34096 (7)
5 'Jubilee' No 45592 (6)
6 BTC, the British ___ Commission, 1947-64 (9)
7 South London station south-east of Peckham Rye (7)
8 'A3' No 60091 (7,6)
15 City where trains entered what was known as Central station across the King Edward Bridge (9)
17 'A2/3' No 60516 (7)
19 *The* ___ *Rifleman*, 'Royal Scot' No 46164 (7)
20 'A3' No 60092, the golfer's favourite? (7)
21 *Ben* ___, Class 60 No 60096 (6)
24 ___ *Hall*, No 6986 (5)

A bridge too far?

Mention was made above of the King Edward Bridge. Can you name the following bridges or viaducts, with the stations at each end given as clues?

1 St Budeaux and Saltash
2 Dalmeny and North Queensferry
3 Three Bridges and Balcombe
4 Kirkby Stephen and Barras
5 Bowness and Annan

Parting of the ways

1 Around which famous Junction station are Latchmere, Longhedge, Ludgate and Falcon Junctions?

2 Over the 14 miles from Waterloo to Hampton Court Junction, there are ten of what particular kind of junction?

3 The name of which Settle & Carlisle junction had 'and Garsdale' added to it in 1900, then the junction name was removed in 1932, leaving just 'Garsdale'. What was the former junction name?

4 Which pre-Grouping 'Junction' line, as its name implied, connected with the Midland Railway at its western end at Broom Junction and at its eastern end at Ravenstone Wood Junction?

5 Which other pre-Grouping 'Junction' line linked Andoversford Junction with Andover Junction?

6 What was the particular significance of the names of junction stations such as Seaton Junction, Sidmouth Junction and Killin Junction?

7 When Verney Junction station, between the LNWR and Metropolitan Railway, was opened in 1868, there was no settlement there – so where did the name come from?

8 Which former Midland Railway station, built on a triangular junction, had Leeds Junction, Bradford Junction and Bingley Junction at the three apexes?

9 Which former London terminus was at the end of a short branch from Dalston Junction?

10 Apart from that to Llandudno, which other branch diverges from the main line at Llandudno Junction?

11 Apart from that to Tiverton, which other branch left the main line at Tiverton Junction?

12 Which station is served by a loop line with Worle Junction and Uphill Junction at its two ends?

13 Kemble was the junction for two GWR Gloucestershire branches – serving which two towns?

14 Which preserved line's most westerly point is Yarwell Junction, although there is no station there?

15 Which pre-Grouping system included Dovey Junction, Moat Lane Junction and Three Cocks Junction?

16 Which city's station is flanked by Pye Wipe, West and East Holmes, Durham Ox and Sincil Junctions?

17 Georgemas Junction is the most northerly in Britain, and is the junction for which town?

18 Kinnaber Junction, north of Montrose, was crucial in which railway event of 1895?

19 The GWR's Cogload Junction was given a flyover during remodelling in 1930-32, on the approach to which station?

20 John Airey first published his *Railway Junction Diagrams* in 1867, based on maps being used by which railway body?

This & that

Many stations serve more than one place, which is reflected in their name. Below are ten examples past and present, but they've been jumbled by placing all the first names and second names in alphabetical order. Can you unscramble the true pairings?

1	Arrochar	&	Badsey
2	Chappell	&	Catterall
3	Garstang	&	Dorridge
4	Glastonbury	&	Four Marks
5	Goring	&	Frampton
6	Grimstone	&	Kirkoswald
7	Knowle	&	Streatley
8	Lazonby	&	Street
9	Littleton	&	Tarbet
10	Medstead	&	Wakes Colne

Crossword No 14

Across

9 and 10 Former Bristol steam shed, 82B (2,7,5)

11 ___ & Swansea Bay Railway, GWR constituent (7)

12 Three-coach set on four bogies, as in the 'Silver Jubilee' train (7)

13 The ___, terminus of a short LB&SCR branch near Brighton (4)

14 Junction of the Bromsgrove and Redditch lines south of Birmingham (5,5)

17 'West Country' No 34102 (7)

18 2-6-2 tank loco (6)

20 Station on the Taff Vale Llantrisant-Aberthaw line (10)

23 *Hal ___ Wynd*, or *Cock ___ North* (1,3)

25 'B1' No 61019 (7)

26 Station between Barmouth and Porthmadog (7)

28 *Ocean ___*, 'A2/3' No 60517 (5)
29 'Jubilee' No 45630 (9)

Down

1 Initials of the company that served Kilmarnock, Ayr and Dumfries (1,1,1,1)
2 'A3' No 60098 (5,3)
3 Creatures after which 'A4s' Nos 60018-34 were originally named (5)
4 and 22 down 'Jubilee' No 45581 (5,3,6)
5 Sheffield, ___-under-Lyne & Manchester Railway, company that built Woodhead Tunnel in 1845 (6)
6 East Coast docks opened by the Great Central Railway in 1912 (9)
7 ___ & Dingle Light Railway, in South West Ireland (6)
8 ___ Moss, peat bog crossed with difficulty by the Liverpool & Manchester Railway (4)
13 ___ Road, the Caledonian Railway's principal loco shed in Edinburgh (5)
15 G. P. ___, influential LNWR Superintendent of the Line, 1874-95 (5)
16 Preserved GWR 4-6-0 No 5952 (5,4)
18 Ryde ___ ___, northernmost station on the Isle of Wight (4,4)
19 *Duke of ___*, 'A2/1' No 60508 (8)
21 ___ *Hall*, No 6919 (6)
22 See 4 down
24 D815, or 'Western' No D1067 (5)
25 and 27 ___ ___ Halt, station on the GNR's Hatfield-St Albans branch (4,4)

Silver service

Mention was made above of the LNER's 1935 streamlined train the 'Silver Jubilee'.

1 The 'Silver Jubilee' linked which city with London King's Cross?

2 Which famous LNER General Manager, in 1934, put in hand plans for a lighter, high-speed express train?

3 Name the four streamlined 'silver' locomotives built to haul the service.

4 By 1938 all four locomotives had been repainted – in what colour?

5 Which other company had named a locomotive *Silver Jubilee* in 1934?

Crossword No 15

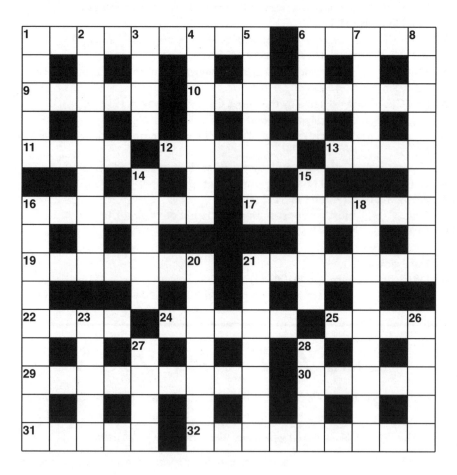

Across

1 Victorian Prime Minister giving his name to a class of LB&SCR 0-4-2s (9)

6 ___ Street, Oldham, Ashton-under-Lyne & Guide Bridge station in Oldham (5)

9 Preserved 'J36' No 65243 (5)

10 Preserved 'West Country' No 34027 (3,6)

11 Nickname for the Class 25 diesels (4)

12 Terminus of a Cambrian Railways branch from Abermule (5)

13 One of the 'Big Four' (1,1,1,1)

16 Former GWR station at Yeovil (3,4)

17 Terminus of a GWR branch from Gwinear Road (7)

19 Terminus of a GER branch from Elsenham (7)

21 Station on the Midland Main Line south of St Albans (7)

22 Type of mountain railway, as that up Snowdon (4)

24 ___ & Farmer, signal engineers (5)
25 ___ Bank, junction for the LNWR's Morecambe branch (4)
29 BR Standard 4-6-0 No 73081 (9)
30 'Jubilee' No 45650 (5)
31 Old ___, test track on a former Midland line in Leicestershire (5)
32 Class 47 No 47737 (9)

Down

1 Fort ___ Halt, on the LSWR's Lee-on-the-Solent branch (5)
2 D215 (9)
3 River giving its name to the preserved line from Aviemore to Boat of Garten (4)
4 ___ Basin and ___ Village, stations on the Wisbech & Upwell Tramway (7)
5 Junction station on the Axholme Joint Railway (7)
6 Steam loco fuel (4)
7 Newcastle ___, terminus of a GWR branch from Pencader (5)
8 Sir ___ ___, General Manager of the Midland Railway, 1906-18, and Chairman of the LMS, 1924-27 (3,6)
14 and 15 ___ of ___, 'Britannia' No 70050 (5,5)
16 Terminus of a GNofSR branch from Maud Junction (9)
18 'D49' 'Hunt' Class No 62740 (3,6)
20 Loco coupling element where 'tractive effort' is often measured (7)
21 Lord ___, 'Britannia' No 70042 (7)
23 ___ Raikes, preserved Mersey Railway 0-6-4T No 5 (5)
26 Midland Main Line junctions between Nottingham and Derby (5)
27 ___ Cross, Midland Main Line junction south of Chesterfield (4)
28 LNWR North Wales main line station and water troughs (4)

Name-calling 2

Diesel locos also gained nicknames, as referred to in 11 across.
Which TOPS classes attracted the following soubriquets?

1 Hoovers

2 Teddy Bears

3 Growlers

4 Whistlers

5 Choppers

Up line, down line

When the answers have been entered into the grid, reading upwards or downwards as indicated, the letters in the tinted squares will spell out the appropriate names of two former GWR locomotives.

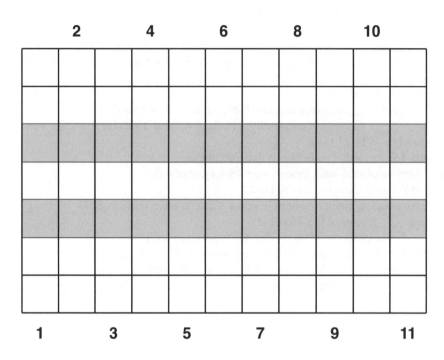

Up

1 Station and tunnel between Worcester and Hereford
3 GER Norfolk station between Wroxham and County School
5 ___ *Walker*, spirited name formerly carried by Class 47 No 47283!
7 *Anti-Aircraft* ___ or *Fighter* ___, 'Battle of Britain' 'Pacifics'
9 'Warship' D844
11 Worcestershire town that has had Hanley Road, Link and Wells stations

Down

2 'West Country' No 34102
4 'Jubilee' No 45736 or Class 86 No 86219
6 Station on the Oban line at the head of the stretch of water of the same name (4,3)
8 Last station before Barking on London's Metropolitan and District Lines (4,3)
10 Former Midland Railway Birmingham shed (2E)

The Big Four: LMS

1 Which Somerset & Dorset station was the furthest south on the LMS system?

2 When Josiah Stamp was appointed to manage the LMS in 1926, which new American-inspired post did he hold?

3 The LMS system was characterised by many tunnels. Which Anglo-Scottish express passed through more than any other British train, 35 in all?

4 The LMS also possessed 35 of what other track feature, more than any other British railway?

5 Which streamlined London-Glasgow express was introduced in July 1937?

6 Stanier's first two 'Pacifics' for the LMS were Nos 6200 and 6201. What were the locomotives' names?

7 These two were followed by ten more, slightly modified, Nos 6203 to 6212. What was unique about the 13th loco, No 6202?

8 Stanier was the first locomotive engineer since Robert Stephenson to be elected a Fellow of which organisation, as indicated on the nameplate of 'Pacific' No 6256, named after him in 1943?

9 The LMS introduced Britain's first main-line diesel-electric locomotives in 1947, Nos 10000 and 10001. In which LMS works were they built?

10 Following the Grouping King George V objected to the Royal Train being repainted in Midland red, so it remained in its old West Coast colours. What were they?

11 Among many newly named LMS trains was the 'Comet' of the 1930s, which ran between London and which city?

12 Which was the biggest marshalling yard on the LMS?

13 The LMS sent a 'Pacific' to the 1939 World's Fair in New York. It carried the number and name 6220 *Coronation*, but was in fact which other member of the class?

14 What was unusual about the three locomotives Nos 4997-9, built in 1927 to haul coal trains from the Midlands?

15 Which LMS constituent company provided it with its busiest suburban line?

16 In 1932 Derby Works took ex-MR 0-6-0T No 1831 and converted it into a very different No 1831 – in what way was it different?

17 An outpost of the LMS at Grouping was the NCC. For what did the initials stand?

18 In 1937, at an establishment in Carlow Street, Mornington Crescent, NW London, the LMS produced 223 million – what?

19 In 1931 the LMS, jointly with the LNER, electrified the line between Manchester and which town?

20 Britain's longest station platform, at 2,194 feet, was built by the LMS to connect which two Manchester stations?

'ell of a mess!

The company's nickname describes the following scrambled LMS nameplates.
Can you correctly assemble the eight names?

1   *The Boy Regiment*

2   *The Border Settlements*

3   *E. Tootal Buccleuch*

4   *Glasgow Glasgow*

5   *Straits Yeomanry*

6   *The Scottish Scout*

7   *City of Horse*

8   *Duchess of Broadhurst*

West Coast whereabouts

Can you find the names of 30 stations on the West Coast Main Line between Euston and Glasgow (inclusive) hidden in this grid of letters? The words may read backwards, forwards, up, down, or diagonally, but always in a straight line and never skipping letters. Not all the letters in the grid are used, while some are used more than once.

```
A N O T R E V L O W L H L A W T S
I N R K W I G A N S C B C P N L R
W O T C C A R N F O R T H T O T I
C T X E Y H O F I W T C L C I M A
R G F E R E I N Y R A A K B T J T
E N T A N G L R O R T E E H C T S
W I Y R W H S H L T R A T N N R R
E R E E H W O I C B S R J M U W A
A R L T S W S L I T O U T G J N C
I A E S O L N E M W E D E L N B B
S W D A E T S P M E H L E M E H E
P W A C S V B A S L E F B T D R A
R A M N G P T C Y Y H O A P S A T
E D R A Z Z U B N O T H G I E L T
S A R L W S G I T W O G S A L G O
T S A D T U W L I C H F I E L D C
O P A S R T T T D R O F S N I W K
N O I T C N U J D R O F T A W F D
B L I S W O R T H D R O F F A T S
```

Across

8 Edinburgh's principal station (8)

9 LNWR station between Corwen and Denbigh (6)

10 Abbreviated name carried by 'Patriot' No 45528 (1,1,1,1)

11 First station after Exeter on the GWR's Teign Valley line (3)

12 Catesby or Combe Down, eg (6)

13 Former standard-gauge terminus where the narrow-gauge South Tynedale Railway is based (6)

15 Midland Railway station south of Nottingham on the Melton Mowbray line (8)

17 Talyllyn Railway station near some famous falls (7)

19 Station on the LSWR's Meon Valley line – with a hedge, it seems! (7)

22 Terminus of a GWR branch from Yarnton (8)

24 North British station on the Alloa-Kinross line that the Americans are keen to protect? (6)

25 ___ & Kinniel Railway, Scottish preserved line (6)

27 *Steady* ___, 'A2/3' No 60512 (3)

28 ___ Vale Railway, South Wales company (4)

29 ___ Tramway, built on a standard-gauge railway trackbed in Devon (6)

30 Terminus of a GWR branch from Newbury (8)

Down

1 Covering 24½ acres, Britain's largest railway station (8)

2 ___ Valley Railway, preserved line near Peterborough (4)

3 'Warship' D803 (6)

4 Former GWR steam shed that became home to the Birmingham Railway Museum (7)

5 ___ *Castle*, No 5094 (8)

6 Windsor & ___ Central or Riverside (4)

7 'A3' No 60101 (6)

14 'Warship' No D854 (5)

16 and 18 Flat road/rail or rail/rail intersection (5,8)

20 ___ Park, Manchester steam shed 9E (8)

21 Ffestiniog Railway station with a spiral 'Deviation' line (6)

23 Name carried by the first Class 89 electric, No 89001 (6)

24 Keighley & Worth Valley Railway station (6)

26 St ___, Junction for the St Ives branch, Cornwall (4)

28 Name carried in the 1960s by No D1671 (4)

Initial thoughts

1 What do the initials forming the answer to 10 across stand for?

2 At a 16 and 18 across you might find AHB – what are they?

3 At 1 down you might have caught a 4-VEP. What structural feature and type of brakes gave rise to 'VEP'?

4 The company that built the line to 22 across was the EGR – what do the initials stand for?

5 'Castle' No 7017 was named *G. J. Churchward*. What were this CME's first two names?

Narrow-minded

1 Which narrow-gauge railway was acquired by the Cambrian Railways in July 1913?

2 Britain has two narrow-gauge mountain railways. One climbs 3,140 feet to the summit of Snowdon, and the other, opened a year earlier, climbs 1,823 feet up which other mountain?

3 Why do Snowdon Mountain Railway locos have forward-tilted boiler and firebox?

4 Which 2ft-gauge railway runs on the trackbed of the former NER standard-gauge Alston branch, closed in 1976?

5 Which famous rectory garden in Leicestershire contains 110 yards of 2ft-gauge line?

6 Which narrow-gauge line became the world's first preserved railway in 1951?

7 Which 15¼-mile 3ft-gauge railway is operated by a fleet of Beyer Peacock 2-4-0Ts?

8 Opened in 1919, what material was the 2ft-gauge Leighton Buzzard Railway originally built to carry?

9 Which 12¼-inch-gauge Welsh line features half-sized replicas of narrow gauge engines *Yeo*, *Sherpa*, *Beddgelert* and *Russell*?

10 Which 2ft-gauge 1¼-mile South Coast line, later converted to 2ft 9in, was the UK's first electric railway?

11 Which line was authorised in 1922, the company having acquired the North Wales Narrow Gauge and Portmadoc, Beddgelert & South Snowdon Railways in 1921?

12 Opened as a tramroad in 1858, this Welsh line had a passenger service from 1880, and was bought by the GWR in 1930, which withdrew the service the following year. It closed completely in 1948, some stock going to the Talyllyn Railway, then re-opened in 1985. Which line is it?

13 Two North Wales narrow-gauge lines have stations called Halfway. One is the Snowdon Mountain Railway, the other a tramway – which?

14 Which line in the South of England was established in the early 1920s by two racing drivers, Capt J. E. P. Howey and Count Zbrowski?

15 Which 2ft-gauge lakeside Welsh line uses the trackbed of the former 4ft-gauge Padarn Railway?

16　Which other 2ft-gauge lakeside Welsh line has the Welsh name Rheilffordd Llyn Tegid?

17　Which line, authorised as 2ft 9in gauge and opened as 3 feet, was bought by Bassett-Lowke in 1915 and converted to 15in-gauge, then preserved in 1960?

18　Which 'Working Museum' established in a former Sussex chalk quarry boasts an extensive collection of narrow-gauge railway equipment?

19　Which narrow-gauge line had to be diverted due to the flooding of the original route by the Llyn Ystradau reservoir scheme?

20　Which 2ft 6in-gauge line was originally operated by two 2-4-0T locos *The Earl* and *The Countess*, named in honour of the occupants of nearby Powis Castle?

Common names II

When the following GWR station names are entered correctly in the grid, their initial letters will spell out something they have in common. However, while they are all linked in some way, one is an odd one out – which, and why?

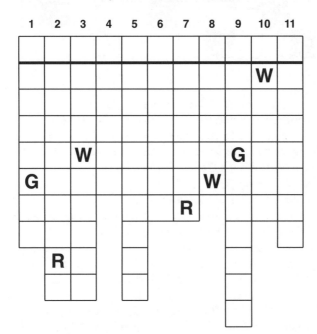

ABBOTSBURY	EVESHAM	SWANSEA
ABERGAVENNY	LAUNCESTON	ST FAGANS
CARDIGAN	LUDLOW	TOTNES
CHESTER	SHREWSBURY	

Number crunching 2

1		2		3		4		5		
		6				7			8
9	10						11	12	
13			14		15		16		17
	18						19		
20			21						22
		23				24			
25	26		27	28		29			30	31
32		33						34	
		35				36			
	37			38				39	

Across

1   ___ *Squadron*, 'Battle of Britain' No 34089 (3)
3   Mallard's record speed in miles per hour achieved in 1938 (3)
5   'B___', LNER class of 4-6-0s also known as 'Sandringhams' (2)
6   21C___, SR number of preserved 'West Country' No 34039 *Boscastle* (3)
7   Wheel arrangement of half a Double Fairlie (1-1-1)
9   D___, 'Warship' *Cockade* (3)
11   Wheel arrangement of the GWR '14XX' Class (1-1-1)
13   TOPS class number of the English Electric Type 4s in the D200 series (2)
14   Number of 'West Country' 'Pacific' *Bere Alston* (5)
17   Class number of 1990s Co-Co electrics named after authors and composers (2)
18   Number of miles between London Euston and Carlisle by the WCML (3)
19   Number of NER 2-2-4T *Aerolite*, preserved in the National Collection (2)
20   Number of SR 'Schools' Class 4-4-0s built (2)
21   TOPS number of the 1959 WCML electric loco E3001 (5)
22   ___A, BR shedcode for York, now incorporated in the NRM … (2)
23   … which opened in September 19__ (2)
24   Ruling gradient of the GCR's London Extension, equating to 30 feet in the mile (3)
25   Number of 'Deltics' built (2)
27   Class 17 across named *J. S. Bach* (5)
30   1 in __¾, gradient of the Lickey Incline (2)

32 D___, Class 20 across *Carmania* (3)
34 Wheel arrangement of the LSWR Beattie well tanks (1-1-1)
35 'Mogul' wheel arrangement (1-1-1)
36 Number of the GWR's French De Glehn compound *La France* (3)
37 Number of arches in Britain's longest viaduct at Harringworth, Northants (2)
38 ___ Marylebone Road, former BRB headquarters (3)
39 GCR number of the preserved 4-4-0 *Butler-Henderson* (3)

Down
1 Number of the preserved GWR 'Modified Hall' *Owsden Hall* (4)
2 D___, *Empress of Britain* (3)
3 Year in which electric services began on the Woodhead route (4)
4 Number of preserved GWR 4-6-0 *King George V* (4)
5 I in ___, gradient for 15 miles of the Settle & Carlisle 'Long Drag' (3)
8 Number of *Evening Star* (5)
10 Traditional time for departure of the 'Cornish Riviera' from Paddington (4)
12 'D__', LNER 'Hunt' Class 4-4-0s (2)
14 BR number of SR 'Lord Nelson' Class *Lord Hood* (5)
15 Number of Gresley's high-pressure 4-6-4 locomotive of 1929 (5)
16 BR number of 'Royal Scot' *Coldstream Guardsman* (5)
20 BR number of *Duchess of Hamilton* (5)
22 LMS number of 'Jubilee' *Trinidad* (4)
26 Daniel Gooch's age when he was appointed Loco Superintendent of the GWR (2)
28 Year in which the Potters Bar crash occurred (4)
29 Number of GWR 'Saint' 4-6-0 *Saint Ambrose* (4)
31 Number of GWR 'Castle' 4-6-0 *Tenby Castle* (4)
33 GWR number of the Welshpool & Llanfair's 0-6-0T *The Earl* (3)
34 'IC ___', ECML Class 91-hauled trains (3)

Pull out the stops

Hidden in the following sentences are the names of stations, which are further clued by the sentences themselves. The first has been solved to show you how the puzzle works

1 South of here the Midland **ent**ered Blea Moor Tunnel.
2 Wait there for down train from Worcester.
3 Where local to north heads along Basingstoke branch.
4 Where there was some panic re Webb's compounds!
5 A super through station to see Edinburgh-Aberdeen expresses.
6 Through which station a train makes a dash for Dover?
7 Where to see *Henry Oakley* or 'King Arthur' *Sir Lamiel*.
8 Station which a westbound train passed on its way to Garsdale.
9 For his Silver Wedding, Wallace travelled from here to Kyle of Lochalsh.
10 Terminus of some of the slowest of the Great Eastern's trains?

Crossword No 17

Across

9 'Jubilees' Nos 45563 … (9)

10 … and 45574 (5)

11 and 8 down S&DJR station in Bath (5,4)

12 Station on the GWR branch from Pontrilas to Hay (9)

13 and 22 down GER station between Audley End and Bartlow (7,6)

14 *Glen ___*, 'D34' No 62488 (7)

17 NER station between Alnwick and Coldstream (5)

19 Initials by which the Southern Railway's famous express to Cornwall and Devon was known (1,1,1)

20 Junction for the GWR's Kingsbridge branch (5)

21 'EM1' electric loco No 26053 (7)

22 First word on the nameplates of the diesel-hydraulics of Class 52 (7)

24 GWR 4-6-0 No 5914 (5,4)

26 'Britannia' No 70017 (5)
28 See 2 down
29 ___ High Level on the Barry Railway, and ___ Low Level on the Taff Vale, as re-named by the GWR in 1924 (9)

Down

1 *Earl* ___, 'Britannia' No 70044 (4)
2 and 28 across   Class 33 No 33050 (4,2,5)
3 ___ ___ & Broseley, GWR Shropshire station where the first was built for road traffic rather than rail! (4,5)
4 *Earl of St* ___, 'Castle' No 5059 (6)
5 Settle & Carlisle line station prefixed 'Hawes Junction and' until 1932 (8)
6 Sir George ___, General Manager of the NER, 1891-1906 (4)
7 *22 across* ___, D1055 (8)
8 See 11 across
13 ___ Stewart & Co, Glasgow locomotive-builders(5)
15 *22 across* ___, No D1051 (9)
16 First word on the nameplates of 'Hall' No 4921, and 'Modified Hall' No 7902 (5)
18 ___ *Community*, Class 86 No 86238 (8)
19 NER station between Northallerton and 5 down (8)
22 See 13 across
23 Maurice ___, distinguished photographer of the GWR, and co-founder of the Railway Photographic Society in 1922 (6)
24 First station on the GSWR west of Gretna Green (4)
25 Number of Elms at a principal Southern Railway shed in London (4)
27 Location of a freight concentration yard opened by the GCR in 1907 (4)

Direction finding

The word providing the answer to 22 across crops up twice more
in the crossword, and also on the nameplates of the following four locomotives –
can you identify the names?

1   'Castle' No 7007, Class 47 No 47500 and Class 43 43185
2   A state on 'Jubilee' No 45568
3   A newspaper on Class 56 No 56038
4   'Britannia' No 70025

Loose-coupled II

More quirky or cryptic links...

1 Why might GWR No 100 (formerly 4009 *Shooting Star*), Kilmarnock engine-builder Andrew, and a Derby-based railway company be of assistance on the Lickey?

2 What is the connection between the surname of an earlier GWR No 100, the owner of the West Somerset's Lydeard, and Stoke, north of Exeter, and what is their collective connection with an express from Paddington to Oxford, Worcester and Hereford?

3 What is the 'alphabetical' connection between a North British station between Berwick and Grantshouse, a station between Nottingham and Trent Junctions, and a tourist Tramway in east Devon?

4 What might a junction west of Hastings be pleased to find in an incline on the Cromford & High Peak Railway?

5 The Brighton line junction for Horsham, the next station east of Ilford, the next station north of Sutton Coldfield, and a GER station between Cambridge and Newmarket combine to become an M&GN station – which?

6 What is the connection between a halt north of Didcot, the station following Bideford and Westward Ho!, and that where Eric Treacy died?

7 What is the national connection between the place lightly linked with Manifold, the *Knight* of 'A3' No 60065, and Grove 24B?

8 What is the connection between GWR 4-6-0 No 5075, the terminus of the Ravenglass & Eskdale Railway, and 'Britannia' No 70014?

9 Why might you come across 'A3' No 60092, 'V2' No 60800's *Arrow* and a tank loco's coal container at a station between Ruislip and Gerrards Cross?

10 Electric No 86259 was the sworn enemy of a station east of Basingstoke, but the latter was more scared of a long, low GWR wagon for carrying boilers, etc – what's the famous play?

11 In what way do an LSWR station south of Meldon and a Spa Valley Railway station unite at a LNWR/MR Joint junction just north of Nuneaton?

12 In what way might you find a Street south of Ashford and a station between Minster and Dover in a refreshment room?

13 What have 'Jubilee' No 45697 and a Monmouth station to do with Brad Pitt?

14 What is the connection between a GWR station east of Whiteball, the terminus of a GWR branch from Kidlington, the LNWR junction for Ebbw Vale, and 'Castles' after 1940/1?

15 What is the horticultural connection between a Worcester station, a set of WCML water troughs south of Watford Junction, and a station between Eastleigh and Fareham?

16 In what way do LNER 'P2' No 2001, a station with a titular link with Keswick and Penrith, and 'Warship' No D810 represent a junction between the Cambrian and the Midland near Hay?

17 What is the connection between a Humberside rail-served ferry pier, 'Merchant Navy' No 35014, and 'Britannia' No 70018?

18 What is the connection between a station on the Colne branch, a 1945-built Barclay 0-4-0ST on the Colne Valley Railway, and 'Jubilee' No 45682?

19 'Britannia' No 70013 and GWR No 6010 met at 8A – in what conflict?

20 What is the connection between 'Jubilee' No 45698, 'Castle' No 7028, and a station between Birmingham New Street and Kings Norton?

Name dropping

Many railway authors and photographers of 'the old school' used only their initials and surnames, and became very well known in that guise. Below are the full first names of ten of them – can you supply the surname in each case?

1 Oswald Stevens
2 Lionel Thomas Caswall
3 Henry Cyril
4 Rev Wilbert
5 Patrick Bruce
6 Cuthbert
7 Richard Callcott
8 Maurice William
9 Peter William Brett
10 Roger Wakeley

Crossword No 18

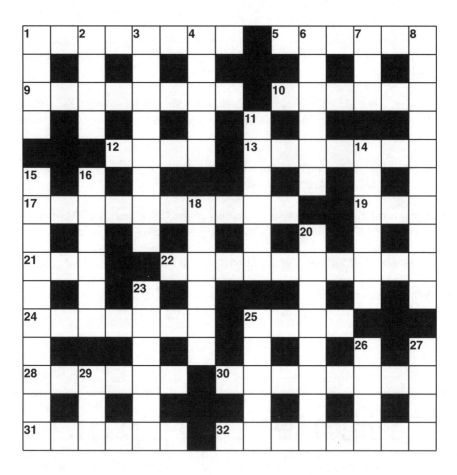

Across

1 Austrian composer commemorated by Class 92 No 92007 (8)

5 and 26 down Preserved steam roundhouse near Chesterfield (6,4)

9 Piccadilly Line station between Ealing and Ruislip (8)

10 and 12 'A3' No 60049 (6,4)

13 ___ *Salopia*, Class 31 No 31147 (7)

17 Central Wales Line station, formerly known as 'High Level' (6,4)

19 Tiny preserved LNWR 18-inch-gauge works loco of 1865 (3)

21 ___ *Wullie*, Class 37 No 37275 (3)

22 West Highland Extension Railway viaduct famously featured in a 'Harry Potter' film! (10)

24 ___ Railway, preserved line with stations at Norden and Harmon's Cross (7)

25 *Maid of* ___, 'D11/2' No 62689 (4)

28 ___ ___ Common, principal shed for Paddington (3,3)
30 North ___, easterly Thames-side terminus of a former GER branch (8)
31 Station at the north end of the Tay Bridge (6)
32 ___ ___ Junction, between the LNWR and the WCKPR south of Penrith (3,5)

Down

1 Famous West Coast Main Line summit (4)
2 ___ Valley line, between Sheffield and Chinley (4)
3 Well-known viaduct and station on the Cambrian Coast line (8)
4 'Jubilee' No 45660 (5)
6 River name of Brush Type 4 D1675 (6)
7 Union formed in 1990 by the amalgamation of the National Unions of Railwaymen and Seamen (1,1,1)
8 *Sir Charles* ___, name carried by Class 20 No 20187, commemorating an electric telegraph pioneer (10)
11 Bridge ___, NBR station between Hilton Junction and Balmano Junction, south of Perth (2,4)
14 Essex terminus of Central Line services since the closure of the line on to Ongar (7)
15 ___ Ferry, intermediate station on the NBR's Selkirk branch (10)
16 and 25 down   'Jubilee' No 45627 (6,5)
18 Type of wheel bearings that *Duke of Gloucester*, eg, runs on (6)
20 ___ ___ *Wedgwood*, 'A4' No 60006 (3,5)
23 *Grand* ___, 'A3' No 60090 (6)
25 See 16 down
26 See 5 across
27 ___ Tryfan, station on the Bryngwyn branch of the North Wales Narrow Gauge Railway/Welsh Highland Railway (4)
29 Bridge of ___, one end of the preserved Caledonian Railway at Brechin (3)

Colour party

It's hopefully not giving too much away to say that a colour is featured
in the answer to 32 across. The following clues lead to names or terms that
include five more colours – can you identify them?

1 Stanier Class 5MT 4-6-0
2 S&DJR Bath station
3 Nickname of the EMUs introduced in 1960 for Glasgow area suburban services
4 Cumbria town that had Bransty and Corkickle stations
5 'A3' No 60043

The National Collection

1 In 1979 a train of ten restored NRM vehicles embarked on a 2,500-mile tour to mark the centenary of what?

2 What is the nickname of the Museum's 1846 Furness Railway 0-4-0 No 3?

3 A 4-8-4 built by the Vulcan Works at Newton-le-Willows for an overseas railway was given back to the Museum by the Government of which country?

4 *Eagle* of 1965 is preserved in the Museum – what is it?

5 'Merchant Navy' No 35029 *Ellerman Lines* is a centrepiece of the Museum's exhibition, for a reason that means it will never run again – why?

6 Preserved Travelling Post Office coach No 186 carries the initials 'WCJS' – what do they stand for?

7 LNER (ex-NER) carriage No 902502 was closely involved in *Mallard*'s 1938 speed record – in what capacity?

8 GWR No 4 was saved for the Collection by BR in 1960. What is it?

9 The Museum's fine 1842 four-wheeled Royal Carriage was used by Queen Victoria's mother. What was her name?

10 The LNWR 2-2-2 'single' No 1868, built in 1845 for the Grand Junction Railway, was formerly No 49 and carried what name?

11 No 673, a 4-2-2 'single' of 1899, was built for which railway company?

12 Britain's first privately preserved standard-gauge steam locomotive was given to the NRM by its owner in 1980. It was built in 1899 as No 1247 for which company?

13 The Museum's *Henry Oakley* was the first of what locomotive wheel arrangement to run in Britain?

14 The name of the son of Lord Faringdon (himself honoured by 'A4' No 60034) had earlier been applied to a 4-4-0 loco built by a company with which both he and his father had been associated, and is now part of the National Collection as No 506. Who was he?

15 When it was withdrawn in 1930 GWR General Manager James Milne 'did not consider the engine to be of outstanding importance', but allowed it to go to the LNER's York Railway Museum. Which famous engine is it?

16 *Duchess of Hamilton* arrived at the NRM on indefinite loan from which leisure company?

17 Which locomotive in the National Collection has 'SOUTHERN 777' on its tender?

18 Which NRM 4-6-0 loco was on display at the Great Western Railway Museum at Swindon from its opening in 1962?

19 Which other GWR 4-6-0 in the National Collection was displayed at the British Empire Exhibition in 1924 alongside a more recent NRM acquisition, *Flying Scotsman*?

20 What is the number of the Midland Railway three-cylinder compound 4-4-0 in the Collection?

Mixed traffic

Discover the names of these eight steam sheds from the anagrams, then enter them in the grid; they appear in alphabetical order. When they are all in place, their eight initial letters can be re-arranged to produce the two-word name of a ninth shed.

1											
2											
3											
4											
5											
6											
7											
8											

1 DATE FILES	**5** UN-NAME 'MELTON' (8,4)
2 I HELD LEG (4,4)	**6** NOW BENT BOAT (6,5)
3 NEVER SINS	**7** A HOT TEN? WHEN? (6,5)
4 LOG THINGS	**8** TALL? YES!

The end!

Appropriately for the last puzzle in the book, this one is all about termini.
When all the station names are in place, their last letters, reading down the last column,
will spell out the name of another terminus.

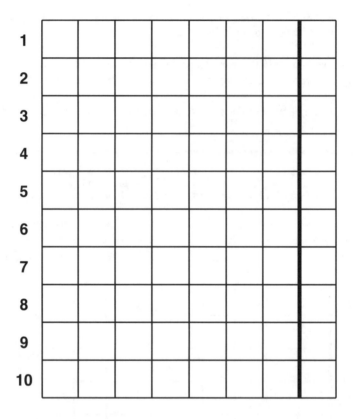

So, which terminus station is at the end of the line or branch from...

1	... Llantrisant (Taff Vale)?
2	... Barmouth (Cambrian)?
3	... Newbury (GWR)?
4	... Norton Fitzwarren (GWR)?
5	... London Paddington (via Plymouth!)?
6	... Welshpool (narrow gauge)?
7	... Kidlington (with Woodstock) (GWR)?
8	... Keighley (MR)?
9	... Aberdeen (Ferryhill) (GNofSR)?
10	... Muir of Ord (HR)?

Solutions

Pioneers (page 7)
1 Tramroad 2 Rainhill 3 Edge Hill 4 Vignoles
5 Isambard 6 Thames 7 Hedley 8 Invicta 9 Cook
10 Killingworth
(Richard) Trevithick

Preserved in steam (page 8)
1 West Somerset Railway 2 It is the botanical name
for watercress, giving the railway its nickname
3 Battle of Bosworth Field, where Henry VII
defeated Richard III 4 Buckinghamshire Railway
Centre, Quainton 5 South Devon Railway
6 Swindon & Cricklade Railway 7 Gloucestershire
Warwickshire Railway 8 Wallingford (Cholsey &
Wallingford Railway) 9 Didcot Railway Centre
10 Dean Forest Railway 11 North Yorkshire Moors
Railway (Grosmont-Goathland) 12 Bluebell Railway
13 Great Central Railway (Leicester North)
14 East Somerset Railway 15 Kent & East Sussex
Railway 16 Bodmin & Wenford Railway 17 Swanage
Railway 18 Nene Valley Railway 19 Paignton &
Dartmouth Railway (Dartmouth is across the river
from the line's terminus at Kingswear) 20 Llangollen
Railway

World celebration! (page 9)
1 Jamaica 2 Ulster 3 Bahamas 4 Indore 5 Leinster
6 Eire 7 Edward
Jubilee (they are all names of LMS 'Jubilee' 4-6-0s)

Crossword No 1 (page 10)
Across: 1 Twenty 4 Edward 9 Drag 10 Blair
11 Moel 12 Pareil 13 Beattock 14 Borderers
16 Boar 17 Pony 18 Scots Grey 22 St David's
23 Active 25 Dent 26 Belle 27 Isle 28 Street
29 Mysore
Down: 1 Tornado 2 Eagle 3 Tubular 5 Durham
6 Armstrong 7 Deepcar 8 Cadbury Castle
15 Doncaster 17 Potters 19 Tracery 20 Enville
21 Ribble 24 Trigo

Odd junction out (page 11)
1 Wotsitt Junction; Thingley Junction (GWR) is west
of Chippenham, Hoo Junction (SECR) is in north
Kent 2 Cat & Fiddle Junction; Dragon Junction (NER)
is in Harrogate, Bo Peep Junction (SECR/LB&SCR) in
Hastings 3 Two Ways Junction; Three Signal Bridge
Junction (GNR/LYR/NER/LNWR) is in Leeds,
Junction Road Junction (THJR) in North London
4 Sparrow Junction; Cuckoo Junction (M&GNR) is in
Spalding, Dove Junction (NSR/GNR) in Burton-upon-
Trent 5 Incline Junction; Over Junction (GWR) is

west of Gloucester, Uphill Junction (GWR) south of
Weston-super-Mare

Crossword No 2 (page 12)
Across: 9 Great Bear 10 Daisy 11 Rutland
12 Tintern 13 Snow 14 John Bunyan 17 Addison
18 Fighter 20 Pearl Diver 23 Peak 25 Sweeney
26 Swansea 28 Eland 29 Llandudno
Down: 1 Ogwr 2 Hertford 3 Atlas 4 Headcorn
5 Triton 6 Edinburgh 7 Sileby 8 Lynn 13 Stamp
15 Norsk 16 Esplanade 18 Frensham 19 Teesside
21 Akeman 22 Inyala 24 Hardy 25 Shed 27 Afon

On the streets (page 13)
1 Birmingham 2 Bolton 3 Nottingham 4 Glasgow
5 Worcester 6 Oldham 7 Cardiff 8 Bury
9 Bradford 10 Pontypool

The Big Four: GWR (page 14)
1 Royal Albert Bridge, Saltash 2 'The Royal Road'
3 'Centenary' stock 4 'Cheltenham Flyer'
5 *Caerphilly Castle* 6 *Windsor Castle* 7 Baltimore &
Ohio 8 Streamlining 9 Slough 10 William Heath
Robinson 11 Brunel timber viaduct, rebuilt in stone
12 Worcester 13 'Hall' Class 14 Halts and
Platforms 15 Hawksworth's 'County' Class 16 Sir
James Milne 17 Old Oak Common, London 18 Sir
Felix Pole 19 *Holiday Haunts* 20 The 'Trip'

Branching out (page 15)
1 Aston Rowant, Watlington 2 Blue Anchor,
Minehead 3 Carbis Bay, St Ives 4 Crymmych Arms,
Cardigan 5 Lustleigh, Moretonhampstead
6 Manorbier, Pembroke Dock 7 Nancegollan,
Helston 8 Rodmarton Platform, Tetbury
9 Uffculme, Hemyock 10 Witney, Fairford

Crossword No 3 (page 16)
Across: 1 Aldeburgh 6 Mungo 9 Clyde 10 Lord
of the 11 Acle 12 Pilot 13 Ayot 16 Haworth
17 Basford 19 Monarch 21 Chester 22 Scot
24 Elgar 25 Unit 29 Elizabeth 30 Owain
31 Dinas 32 Kimberley
Down: 1 Accra 2 Drysllwyn 3 Blea 4 Raleigh
5 Hurcomb 6 Moor 7 Nethy 8 Owen Tudor
14 Truro 15 Isles 16 Hampstead 18 Olton Hall
20 Holbeck 21 Clapham 23 Orion 26 Tenby
27 Mars 28 Dome

Elgar enigma! (page 17)

92009 - 50007 = 42002 - 7005 = 34997 - 14 letters = 34983; delete the first 3 = 4983, the number of GWR 'Hall' Class *Albert Hall*.

Crossword No 4 (page 18)

Across: 8 Ark Royal **9** Iseult **10** Lawn **11** Tay **12** Verney **13** Meldon **15** Observer **17** Empress **19** Compton **22** Talyllyn **24** Amadis **25** Thelma **27** Bat **28** King **29** James I **30** Lavenham
Down: 1 Great Elm **2** Wren **3** Lynton **4** Clayton **5** Sir Visto **6** Seer **7** Cleeve **14** Derby **16** REPTA **18** Sylvania **20** Oriental **21** And Ball **23** Ashpan **24** Active **26** Leek **28** Kent

First name terms (page 19)

1 Rhondda **2** Maryport **3** Shropshire **4** City **5** Leicester **6** Preston **7** Garstang **8** East **9** Wisbech **10** Campbeltown

Tunnel vision (page 20)

1 Moorcock **2** Blea Moor **3** Bramhope **4** Dove Holes **5** Buckhorn **6** Culgaith **7** Hampstead **8** Hastings **9** Thackley **10** Pleasant Copenhagen (King's Cross)

Bridges (page 21)

1 Severn Valley Railway **2** Newcastle-upon-Tyne **3** Woodhead **4** West Highland line (Crianlarich-Fort William) **5** North of Exeter St David's; SR Waterloo-bound trains ran south into Exeter, while GWR Paddington-bound trains were heading north **6** Northampton **7** Bristol Temple Meads **8** Vale of Rheidol Railway **9** Victoria **10** Robert Stephenson **11** Liverpool & Manchester **12** London & Greenwich Railway **13** They are all swing bridges **14** Chepstow **15** Conwy **16** Midland & Great Northern **17** Tay Bridge **18** Stone **19** Somerset & Dorset Joint Railway **20** Ballachulish

Level crossings (page 22)

1 Gwinear Road **2** Lime Street **3** Long Melford **4** Shepherds Well

Summit search (page 23)

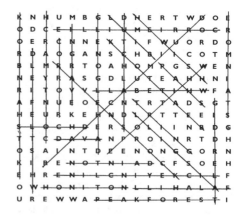

Crossword No 5 (page 24)

Across: 9 Alexandra **10** Uther **11** Envoy **12** Adlestrop **13** Bulleid **14** Sceptre **17** Radio **19** Ree **20** Sands **21** Enfield **22** Kingham **24** Staverton **26** Works **28** Cocks **29** Cranleigh
Down: 1 Yate **2** Yeovil **3** Marylebone **4** Edward **5** Carlisle **6** Pugs **7** Churston **8** Trip **13** Burke **15** Easingwold **16** Epsom **18** Defiance **19** Radstock **22** Kendal **23** Hermit **24** SECR **25** East **27** Soho

Triple chance (page 25)

1 Sheffield **2** Chesterfield **3** Leeds **4** Swansea **5** Exeter **6** Southport **7** Cheltenham **8** Folkestone **9** Yarmouth **10** Dundee

Railwaymen (page 26)

1 ICI **2** Sir Robert McAlpine **3** Sir Daniel Gooch **4** O. S. Nock **5** Claud Hamilton **6** Charles Benjamin **7** A knighthood **8** David Joy **9** Richard (Lord) Marsh **10** Pullman **11** Hotels and refreshment rooms **12** Francis Webb **13** The brick arch **14** 'Atlantic' 4-4-2 **15** William Stanier **16** LNWR **17** R. A. Riddles **18** Ivo Peters **19** L. T. C. (Tom) Rolt **20** Sir Eustace Missenden

Sir names (page 27)

1 Sir Alexander Erskine-Hill **2** Sir Brian Robertson **3** Sir Christopher Wren **4** Sir Frederick Pile **5** Sir Henry Johnson **6** Sir Herbert Walker KCB **7** Sir James Milne **8** Sir Keith Park **9** Sir Murrough Wilson **10** Sir Robert McAlpine

Crossword No 6 (page 28)
Across: 1 Belpaire 5 Thomas 9 Rise Hill 10 Alfred 12 High 13 Rheidol 17 Black Watch 19 DVT 21 R. E. L. 22 Princetown 24 Ontario 25 Peak 28 Impala 30 Victoria 31 Norris 32 Merehead
Down: 1 Bury 2 Liss 3 Ashwicke 4 Ralph 6 Holden 7 MGR 8 Saddle tank 11 Brecon 14 Didcot 15 Aberdonian 16 Tablet 18 Aureol 20 Lemaitre 23 Ardlui 25 Prime 26 Urie 27 Yard 29 Par

Back and forth (page 29)
1 7007 2 70007 3 34043 4 43034 5 6006 6 60006 7 60106 8 5005 9 50005 10 47774

Diesels (page 30)
1 Fairburn 2 The 'Deltics'; engines by Napier & Son 3 Class 35 'Hymek' 4 Switzerland 5 LMS 'Patriots' and 'Royal Scots' 6 D200 (later 40122) 7 50035 (formerly D435) *Ark Royal* 8 'Warship' (D821 *Greyhound*) 9 Class 52 (D1023 *Western Fusilier*) 10 Crewe 11 Class 08 (the loco became D3000) 12 A1A-A1A (only the outer two axles on each bogie being powered) 13 English Electric 14 The 'Condor' 15 London Paddington-Bristol-South Wales 16 London, Ontario, Canada 17 You can 'see through them' from one side to the other 18 Class 37 19 Romania 20 Class 60

Common names 1 (page 31)
1 Warrior 2 Enterprise 3 Sentinel 4 Talisman 5 Empire 6 Regent 7 Nobleman
Western (the word that precedes them as names of Western Region diesel-hydraulics)

Number crunching 1 (page 32)
Across: 1 100 3 601 5 12 6 4-6-2 7 990 9 2-6-2 11 350 13 31 14 60532 17 50 18 0-6-0 19 50 20 60 21 87002 22 52 23 24 24 600 25 08 27 73115 30 45 32 222 34 125 35 214 36 251 37 55 38 0-8-0 39 123
Down: 1 1023 2 0-4-2 3 6220 4 1923 5 103 8 40012 10 6100 12 55 14 60847 15 50031 16 25265 20 60022 22 5042 26 82 28 3440 29 1020 31 5593 33 225 34 111

Out of town (page 33)
1 Dalston 2 Clapham 3 Richmond 4 Stratford 5 Vauxhall 6 Hammersmith 7 Charing Cross
They all share their names with stations in and around London

Crossword No 7 (page 34)
Across: 1 Edward I 5 Worksop 9 Pye Hill 10 Aby 11 Run 12 Eddystone 14 Louth 15 South 17 Mark Cross 19 Pendennis 21 Toads

24 Lovat 25 Regulator 27 Oil 28 EPB 29 Old Ford 31 Twerton 32 Eastern
Down: 1 Express 2 Wye 3 Rails 4 Isle of Man 5 Whale 6 Royal Scot 7 Sir Hugo 8 Penrhos 13 Dhu 16 Hoe Street 18 Rose Grove 19 Polmont 20 Neville 22 APT 23 Sarsden 25 Robin 26 Ladas 30 Ore

The long and the short (page 35)
1 Horwich (LYR) 2 'V2' 3 Highland Light Infantry (the full name was *Highland Light Infantry, City of Glasgow Regiment*) 4 Thor 4 Gnu

Down main 1: Southern (page 36)
1 West Wickham 2 Eastleigh 3 The Dyke 4 New Romney 5 Red Posts 6 Plymouth 7 North Tawton 8 Mortehoe
Waterloo; Weymouth

The Big Four: Southern Railway (page 37)
1 It was the only all-Pullman electric train 2 Seven: Waterloo, Cannon Street, Charing Cross, Holborn Viaduct, Blackfriars, London Bridge and Victoria 3 Headlands (eg *Beachy Head*, *South Foreland*) 4 Halwill Junction 5 Lynton & Barnstaple Railway 6 Concrete 7 Chessington 8 Queen Street 9 A pantry car 10 4-6-0 No E850 *Lord Nelson* 11 'Schools' 12 Nigel Gresley, on the LNER 13 The number of coupled axles 14 'Golden Arrow'/'Flèche d'Or' 15 A Channel Tunnel 16 Sir Herbert Walker 17 RMS *Queen Mary* 18 Feltham 19 'Atlantic Coast Express' 20 The box-pattern (non-spoked) driving wheels

Fit the Bill (page 38)
1 William Hedley 2 *Captain Bill Smith RNR* 3 G. J. Churchward 4 William Shakespeare and William Wordsworth 5 William Whitelaw

Hoover hunt! (page 39)

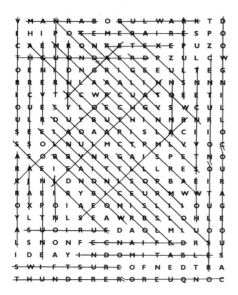

The locomotives to be found are: Achilles, Agincourt, Ajax, Anson, Ark Royal, Barham, Benbow, Bulwark, Centurion, Collingwood, Conqueror, Courageous, Dauntless, Defiance, Dreadnought, Eagle, Exeter, Fearless, Formidable, Furious, Glorious, Hercules, Hood, Howe, Illustrious, Implacable, Indomitable, Invincible, Leviathan, Lion, Monarch, Neptune, Ramillies, Renown, Repulse, Resolution, Revenge, Rodney, Royal Oak, St Vincent, Superb, Swiftsure, Temeraire, Thunderer, Tiger, Triumph, Valiant, Vanguard, Victorious, and Warspite.

Crossword No 8 (page 40)

Across: 4 Ash 8 Coventry 9 Arthur 10 Falcon 11 E. C. Trench 13 Rowant 14 Long Toms 15 Elie 16 Elsted 18 Barons 21 Rhyl 22 Evershot 24 Elsham 26 Osterley 29 Holmes 30 Gatien 31 Railtour 32 Esk
Down: 1 Tobago 2 Merchant 3 Stansted 4 Ayre 5 Hart 6 Street 7 Dutchman 12 Croe 13 Rye 14 Light 17 Levisham 18 Blenheim 19 Resolute 20 Sam 21 Rose 23 Reekie 25 Avenue 27 Lane 28 York

Preserved stations (page 41)

1 Battlefield Line 2 Great Central Railway 3 Bodmin & Wenford Railway 4 Keighley & Worth Valley Railway 5 East Lancashire Railway 6 East Somerset Railway 7 Nene Valley Railway 8 Severn Valley Railway 9 Swanage Railway 10 Llangollen Railway

Crossword No 9 (page 42)

Across: 1 Crystal 5 Palace 9 Coryton 10 Minerva 11 Cam 12 Byron 13 Examine 14 NER 15 Reading 17 Noel 21 Barr 24 Granite 27 Eli 28 Islands 29 Tulse 30 Off 31 Central 32 Ormside 33 Steele 34 Dursley
Down: 1 Cockburn 2 York Road 3 Toton 4 Lancing 5 Pommern 6 Lenwade 7 Corris 8 Raven 16 NUR 18 Our 19 Mill Hill 20 Cemetery 22 Aintree 23 Resolve 24 Gifford 25 Birch 26 Planet 29 Tamar

Guessed houses (page 43)

1 Adelphi, Liverpool (MR) 2 Grosvenor, London (Victoria) (LB&SCR) 3 North Euston, Fleetwood (L&YR) 4 Royal Victoria, Sheffield (GCR) 5 Terminus, Brighton (LB&SCR) 6 Tregenna Castle, St Ives (GWR) 7 Welcombe, Stratford-upon-Avon (LMS)

Loose-coupled I (page 44)

1 Ware, (James) Watt and *Howe* 2 Latimer 3 Steam locomotive types: Pacific, Mogul and Prairie 4 Apex, Summit, 'Peak' 5 Playing cards: (*Brown*) *Jack*, Queen Street, 'King' Class, and 'ACE' ('Atlantic Coast Express') 6 They are makes of car: Ford, Vauxhall and Rover 7 (*Sir*) *Kay* (K), Eye (I), Dee (D) = KID 8 'Bobby' (Bobbie), *Phyllis* and (*Blue*) *Peter*, the trio in *The Railway Children* by E. Nesbit, in which the railway is called the Northern & Southern Railway 9 Brush, Broom and 'Hoover' 10 Top: TOPS, 'Toplights' and Top Shed 11 (The) Dyke, (*E. C.*) *Trench*, and 'the Drain' 12 London termini: Euston, Waterloo and Victoria 13 'Jazz' service, 'pop' safety valves, and Rock (Ferry) 14 Flying: *Flying Fox*, *Flying Dutchman*, and a 'flying junction' 15 Eric: Sykes (W. R.), Idle and Morecambe 16 Metro: 'Metro' tanks, 'Metroland', and Metrolink 17 All have dog nicknames: Pug, Bulldog and Greyhound 18 Royal homes: 'Sandringham' Class, *Balmoral*, *Windsor Castle* 19 *Drake*, 'Duck', *Mallard* 20 Oak: *Royal Oak*, Old Oak Common, Oakworth

In short (page 45)

1 Association of Railway Preservation Societies 2 Associated Society of Locomotive Engineers & Firemen 3 Automatic Warning System 4 Birmingham Railway Carriage & Wagon (Co) 5 British Transport Commission 6 Dublin Area Rapid Transit 7 Driving Van Trailer 8 General Utility Van 9 Historical Model Railway Society 10 London Underground Ltd 11 National Carriers Ltd 12 Permanent way slack 13 Railway Clearing House 14 Railway Operating Division (WWI) 15 Stephenson Locomotive Society 16 Steam Locomotive Operators' Association 17 Traction Maintenance Depot 18 Total Operations Processing System 19 Venice Simplon-Orient Express 20 Working timetable

Crossword No 10 (page 46)

Across: 1 Lydham Manor 9 Worcester 10 Drain
11 Hussar 12 Charlton 13 Maindy 15 Dartmoor
18 Grotrian 19 Stream 21 Medstead 23 Mellis
26 Baker 27 Lord Hawke 28 Eynsham Hall
Down: 1 Lowdham 2 Doris 3 Alexander 4 Mite
5 Northiam 6 Radyr 7 Ventnor 8 Gartmore
14 Iron Duke 16 Tattenham 17 Ian Allan
18 Gemsbok 20 Muswell 22 Torre 24 Lowca
25 Arch

Same name, different loco (page 47)

1 *Sans Pareil* (sometimes one word) 2 Mercury and
Jupiter; Earth! 3 Great Central 4 Class 60
5 *Caerphilly Castle*

Crossword No 11 (page 48)

Across: 1 Lancaster 8 Pom Pom 9 Euston
12 Gate 13 Arrow 14 Edge 17 Manston
18 Hackney 19 Matilda 22 Beamish 24 Ouse
25 Hixon 26 Clan 29 Heriot 30 Levens
31 Blackwell
Down: 2 Alps 3 Cameron 4 St Enoch 5 East
6 Bolton 7 Golden 10 Agamemnon 11 Penyghent
15 Stall 16 Ocean 20 Tisted 21 Asiatic 22 Book
Law 23 Island 27 Hill 28 Oval

Name-calling 1 (page 49)

1 LNWR (Webb 0-6-0s) 2 BR ('9F' 2-10-0s) 3 GCR
(4-4-0s, later LNER 'D10') 4 LMS (Ivatt 4MT 4-6-0s)
5 LSWR (Drummond 4-4-0s) 6 GER (Holden 'T19'
2-4-0s) 7 GNR (Gresley 2-6-0s) 8 SR (Bulleid's 'air-
smoothed' 'Pacifics') 9 MR (4-2-2 single-wheelers)
10 SECR (Maunsell Class 'N' 2-6-0s)

Titled trains (page 50)

1 'Irish Mail' 2 'Cornish Riviera' 3 2pm
4 'Executive' 5 'Scot' 6 'Bin Liner' 7 London and
Cardiff 8 'Elizabethan' 9 'Pines Express' 10 'Belle'
11 Manchester: the 'Manchester Pullman'
12 'Master Cutler' 13 They were operated by 'Blue
Pullman' DMU sets 14 Trent 15 She was known as
Mary, Queen of Scots, and the Pullman train was
named 'Queen of Scots' in 1927 16 A fibreglass
winged thistle 17 'Bristolian' 18 They were all
named after novels by Sir Walter Scott 19 Harwich
20 London and Birmingham

In shape (page 51)

1 Square: Forster Square station 2 Triangle: the
station platforms served all lines on a triangular
junction 3 Circle: all stations on London's Circle
Line 4 Oval: station on the Northern Line 5 Star:
member of the GWR's 'Star' Class of 4-6-0s
6 Diamond: diamond crossing

Tri-composite (page 52)

1 Totnes 2 Schubert 3 Highland 4 Severn
5 InterCity 6 Steinbok 7 Waterloo 8 Whitby
9 Fletcher 10 Beethoven 11 Prairie 12 Regulator
13 Longsight 14 Tregenna 15 Sandsend
'This is the biggest electric train set any boy ever had!'

Railways on screen (page 53)

1 Nene Valley Railway 2 Bluebell Railway
3 Carnforth 4 L&MR *Lion* 5 King's Cross 6 Ford
Anglia 7 No 5972 *Olton Hall* 8 Forth Bridge
9 Victoria Bridge across the Severn, Severn Valley
Railway 10 Buggleskelly 11 'This is the night mail
crossing the border' (*Night Mail*) 12 The Great Train
Robbery (the film was *Robbery* starring Stanley
Baker) 13 Dublin 14 Arley 15 Arnold Ridley
(Private Godfrey) 16 Marylebone 17 Longmoor
Military Railway 18 It was one of the locos that
hauled the 'Fifteen Guinea Special' on 11 August
1968 19 Patrick Whitehouse 20 (*Snowdrift at*)
Bleath Gill

Flower power (page 54)

1 Bluebell 2 Lavender 3 Rose 4 Primrose 5 Thistle
6 Daisy 7 Flax 8 Ivy 9 Vine 10 Lily

Capital quest (page 55)

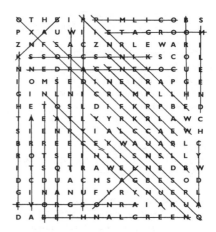

Down main 2: LNER (page 56)

1 Dalmeny 2 Howard 3 Norwich 4 Acklington
5 Aldeburgh 6 Saxmundham 7 Tyndrum 8 New
England 9 Grantham
Doncaster; Edinburgh

The Big Four: LNER (page 57)

1 Great Central Railway 2 William Whitelaw 3 Sir
Ralph Wedgwood 4 Eric Gill (Gill Sans) 5 4-6-4
6 'D49' Hunt' 4-4-0s 7 Whitemoor 8 'Northern
Belle' 9 They were articulated, adjoining carriages
sharing a common bogie 10 The opening panels at

the front giving access to the smokebox **11** The first non-stop London-Edinburgh run of the 'Flying Scotsman', hauled by the locomotive of the same name **12** *Cock o' the North* **13** 'Queen of Scots' **14** Midland Railway **15** It was an electric locomotive built in 1940 for the Sheffield-Manchester electrification, completion of which was delayed by the Second World War **16** To watch films – it was the 44-seat 'LNER-Pathe Cinema Car' **17** They were old stage-coach names **18** Wembley Stadium **19** Worsborough, near Wath **20** *Sir Nigel Gresley*

London A to Z (page 58)

1 Oxford Circus **2** Edgware Road **3** Earls Court **4** Baker Street **5** Camden Town **6** Notting Hill Gate **7** Leicester Square **8** Covent Garden **9** Shepherds Bush **10** Piccadilly Circus

Mind the gap! (page 59)

Across: 2 Abbot **6** Keys **7** Ayre **8** Harry **11** BBC **13** Ian **15** Oxenden **16** Ayr **17** Taw **18** Fairlie **19** Ree **21** Roy **23** Marsh **26** Rose **27** Eden **28** Green
Down: 1 Webb **2** Ash **3** Bar **4** Tay **5** Brea **9** America **10** Riddles **11** Blair **12** Corfe **13** Inter **14** Newby **20** Eton **22** Owen **23** Meg **24** Rye **25** Hen

Crossword No 12 (page 60)

Across: 7 New Street **8** Gable **10** Edmonton **11** Lamiel **12** Skye **13** Engineer **15** Fusible **17** St Mawes **20** Skegness **22** Lile **25** Etarre **26** Fearless **27** Selby **28** Britannia
Down: 1 Leeds **2** O. S. Nock **3** Fritwell **4** Leander **5** Tasmania **6** Blue Peter **9** Plug **14** Musketeer **16** Ingersby **18** Talgarth **19** Ashford **21** Eden **23** Lelant **24** Islip

All Saints (page 61)

1 St Rollox **2** St Albans **3** St Helens **4** *Saint Martin* **5** *St Paddy* **6** St Enoch **7** *Saint Mungo*

Crossword No 13 (page 62)

Across: 1 Abbots **4** Ripton **9** LSWR **10** Eland **11** Anne **12** Mikado **13** Thruster **14** Llanberis **16** Lord **17** Howe **18** Scraptoft **22** Achanalt **23** Turpin **25** Slot **26** Dolls **27** Down **28** Arenig **29** Ashley
Down: 1 Ais Gill **2** Burma **3** Trevone **5** Indore **6** Transport **7** Nunhead **8** Captain Cuttle **15** Newcastle **17** Hycilla **19** Artists **20** Fairway **21** Macdui **24** Rydal

A bridge too far? (page 63)

1 Royal Albert Bridge **2** Forth Bridge **3** Ouse Viaduct **4** Belah Viaduct **5** Solway Viaduct

Parting of the ways (page 64)

1 Clapham Junction **2** Flying junction (fly-overs and fly-unders) **3** Hawes Junction **4** Stratford-upon-Avon & Midland Junction Railway **5** Midland & South Western Junction Railway **6** They were junctions *for* the places named, not stations situated *in* those places **7** It was named after the local landowner, Sir Harry Verney (whose name, before succeeding to the Verney estates, had been Calvert, the derivation of the nearby GCR station, where there was also no settlement) **8** Shipley **9** Broad Street (NLR) **10** The Blaenau Ffestiniog branch **11** The Hemyock branch **12** Weston-super-Mare **13** Tetbury and Cirencester **14** Nene Valley Railway **15** Cambrian Railways **16** Lincoln **17** Thurso **18** The railway Races to the North; it was where the West Coast and East Coast routes to Aberdeen converged **19** Taunton **20** Railway Clearing House

This & that (page 65)

1 Arrochar & Tarbet **2** Chappell & Wakes Colne **3** Garstang & Catterall **4** Glastonbury & Street **5** Goring & Streatley **6** Grimstone & Frampton **7** Knowle & Dorridge **8** Lazonby & Kirkoswald **9** Littleton & Badsey **10** Medstead & Four Marks

Crossword No 14 (page 66)

Across: 9 St Philips **10** Marsh **11** Rhondda **12** Triplet **13** Dyke **14** Barnt Green **17** Lapford **18** Prairie **20** Ystradowen **23** O'the **25** Nilghai **26** Harlech **28** Swell **29** Swaziland
Down: 1 GSWR **2** Spion Kop **3** Birds **4** Bihar and **5** Ashton **6** Immingham **7** Tralee **8** Chat **13** Dalry **15** Neele **16** Cogan Hall **18** Pier Head **19** Rothesay **21** Tylney **22** Orissa **24** Druid **25** Nast **27** Hyde

Silver service (page 67)

1 Newcastle **2** Sir Ralph Wedgwood **3** *Silver Link*, *Quicksilver*, *Silver King*, *Silver Fox* **4** Blue **5** LMS (No 5552)

Crossword No 15 (page 68)

Across: 1 Gladstone **6** Clegg **9** Maude **10** Taw Valley **11** Rats **12** Kerry **13** LNER **16** Pen Mill **17** Helston **19** Thaxted **21** Radlett **22** Rack **24** Saxby **25** Hest **29** Excalibur **30** Blake **31** Dalby **32** Resurgent
Down: 1 Gomer **2** Aquitania **3** Spey **4** Outwell **5** Epworth **6** Coal **7** Emlyn **8** Guy Granet **14** Firth **15** Clyde **16** Peterhead **18** The Bedale **20** Drawbar **21** Roberts **23** Cecil **26** Trent **27** Clay **28** Aber

Name-calling 2 (page 69)

1 Class 50 **2** Class 14 **3** Class 37 **4** Class 40 **5** Class 20

Up line, down line (page 70)
Up: 1 Ledbury **3** Cawston **5** Johnnie **7** Command **9** Spartan **11** Malvern
Down: 2 Lapford **4** Phoenix **6** Loch Awe **8** East Ham **10** Saltley
Upton Castle; *Downham Hall*

The Big Four: LMS (page 71)
1 Bath Green Park **2** President of the Executive **3** 'Thames-Clyde Express', London St Pancras to Glasgow St Enoch via the Settle & Carlisle line **4** Water-troughs **5** 'Coronation Scot' **6** *The Princess Royal* and *Princess Elizabeth* **7** It was Stanier's steam-turbine 'Turbomotive' **8** Royal Society (*Sir William A. Stanier FRS*) **9** Derby **10** Chocolate and white **11** Manchester **12** Toton **13** 6229 *Duchess of Hamilton*, now preserved **14** They were Beyer Garratt 2-6-0+0-6-2s **15** London, Tilbury & Southend line **16** It was rebuilt as an 0-6-0 diesel-hydraulic shunter **17** Northern Counties Committee (system in Northern Ireland that had amalgamated with the MR in 1903) **18** Tickets **19** Altrincham **20** Victoria and Exchange

'ell of a mess! (page 72)
1 *The Boy Scout* (46169) **2** *The Border Regiment* (46136) **3** *E. Tootal Broadhurst* (45534) **4** *Glasgow Yeomanry* (45158) **5** *Straits Settlements* (45629) **6** *The Scottish Horse* (46129) **7** *City of Glasgow* (46242) **8** *Duchess of Buccleuch* (46230)

West Coast whereabouts (page 73)

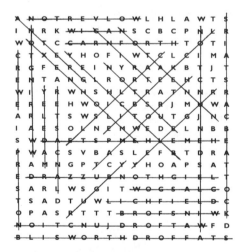

The stations to be found are: Euston, Willesden Junction, Watford Junction, Hemel Hempstead, Tring, Leighton Buzzard, Bletchley, Wolverton, Blisworth, Rugby, Nuneaton, Tamworth, Lichfield, Rugeley, Stafford, Madeley, Crewe, Winsford, Warrington, Wigan, Preston, Lancaster, Carnforth, Oxenholme, Carlisle, Gretna, Lockerbie, Beattock, Carstairs, and Glasgow.

Crossword No 16 (page 74)
Across: 8 Waverley **9** Ruthin **10** REME **11** Ide **12** Tunnel **13** Alston **15** Edwalton **17** Dolgoch **19** Privett **22** Fairford **24** Dollar **25** Bo'ness **27** Aim **28** Taff **29** Seaton **30** Lambourn
Down: 1 Waterloo **2** Nene **3** Albion **4** Tyseley **5** Tretower **6** Eton **7** Cicero **14** Tiger **16** Level **18** Crossing **20** Trafford **21** Dduallt **23** Avocet **24** Damems **26** Erth **28** Thor

Initial thoughts (page 75)
1 Royal Electrical & Mechanical Engineers **2** Automatic Half Barriers **3** Vestibule and Electro-Pneumatic **4** East Gloucestershire Railway **5** George Jackson

Narrow-minded (page 76)
1 Vale of Rheidol **2** Snaefell, Isle of Man **3** To keep the water level horizontal on the 1 in 5½ ruling gradient **4** South Tynedale Railway **5** Cadeby (the late Rev Teddy Boston's collection) **6** Talyllyn Railway **7** Isle of Man Railway **8** Sand **9** Fairbourne Railway **10** Volks Electric Railway, Brighton **11** Welsh Highland Railway **12** Corris Railway **13** Great Orme Tramway, Llandudno **14** Romney, Hythe & Dymchurch Railway **15** Llanberis Lake Railway **16** Bala Lake Railway **17** Ravenglass & Eskdale Railway **18** Amberley Working Museum **19** Ffestiniog Railway **20** Welshpool & Llanfair Railway

Common names II (page 77)
1 Cardigan **2** Abbotsbury **3** Shrewsbury **4** Totnes **5** Launceston **6** Evesham **7** Chester **8** Ludlow **9** Abergavenny **10** Swansea **11** St Fagans
Castle Class: they are all 'Castle' names in the class except Evesham, which is an 'Abbey'

Number crunching 2 (page 78)
Across: 1 602 **3** 126 **5** 17 **6** 139 **7** 0-4-0 **9** 810 **11** 0-4-2 **13** 40 **14** 34104 **17** 92 **18** 300 **19** 66 **20** 40 **21** 81001 **22** 50 **23** 75 **24** 176 **25** 22 **27** 92024 **30** 37 **32** 218 **34** 2-4-0 **35** 2-6-0 **36** 102 **37** 82 **38** 222 **39** 506
Down: 1 6984 **2** 210 **3** 1954 **4** 6000 **5** 100 **8** 92220 **10** 1030 **12** 49 **14** 30859 **15** 10000 **16** 46114 **20** 46229 **22** 5634 **26** 21 **28** 2002 **29** 2912 **31** 7026 **33** 822 **34** 225

Pull out the stops (page 79)
1 Dent **2** Hereford **3** Alton **4** Crewe **5** Perth **6** Ashford **7** York **8** Hawes **9** Dingwall **10** Lowestoft

Crossword No 17 (page 80)
Across: 9 Australia **10** India **11** Green
12 Westbrook **13** Saffron **14** Aladale **17** Akeld
19 ACE **20** Brent **21** Perseus **22** Western
24 Ripon Hall **26** Arrow **28** Grain **29** Treforest
Down: 1 Haig **2** Isle of **3** Iron Bridge **4** Aldwyn
5 Garsdale **6** Gibb **7** Advocate **8** Park **13** Sharp
15 Ambassador **16** Eaton **18** European
19 Aysgarth **22** Walden **23** Earley **24** Rigg
25 Nine **27** Wath

Direction finding (page 81)
The word is 'Western': **1** *Great Western* **2** *Western
Australia* **3** *Western Mail* **4** *Western Star*

Loose-coupled II (page 82)
1 They are all 'bankers': *Lloyds*, Barclay and Midland
2 (William) Dean, Bishop ('s Cleeve), (Stoke) Canon;
'Cathedrals Express' **3** Ayton ('A'), Beeston ('B'),
Seaton ('C') **4** Sheep: Bo Peep and Sheep Pasture
5 Twenty: Three Bridges plus Seven Kings plus Four
Oaks plus Six Mile Bottom **6** Apple: Appleford,
Appledore, Appleby **7** UK national emblems: Leek,
Thistle, Rose **8** *Wellington*, Boot, *Iron Duke*
(nickname of the Duke of Wellington) **9** *Fairway*,
Green (Arrow), bunker; Denham Golf Club **10** *Peter
Pan*: name of loco, Hook, Crocodile (telegraphic
code) **11** In marriage: Bridestowe, Groombridge,
Weddington **12** Ham (Street), Sandwich **13** *Achilles*,
Troy (2004 movie in which Pitt stars as Achilles)
14 'Castles' renamed after WWII aircraft:
Wellington, Blenheim and *Beaufort* **15** Shrub (Hill),
Bushey, Hedge (End) **16** Three Cocks: *Cock o' the
North, Cockermouth, Cockade* **17** The Netherlands:
New Holland, *Nederland Line, Flying Dutchman*
18 Nelson, *Victory, Trafalgar* **19** English Civil War:
Oliver Cromwell, King Charles I, Edge Hill (shed – first
battle of the war was at Edgehill, Warks)
20 Chocolate: *Mars, Cadbury (Castle)*, Bournville

Name dropping (page 83)
1 Nock **2** Rolt **3** Casserley **4** Awdry
5 Whitehouse **6** Hamilton Ellis **7** Riley **8** Earley
9 Semmens **10** Kidner

Crossword No 18 (page 84)
Across: 1 Schubert **5** Barrow **9** Alperton
10 Galtee **12** More **13** Floreat **17** Builth Road
19 Pet **21** Oor **22** Glenfinnan **24** Swanage
25 Lorn **28** Old Oak **30** Woolwich **31** Dundee
32 Red Hills
Down: 1 Shap **2** Hope **3** Barmouth **4** Rooke
6 Amazon **7** RMT **8** Wheatstone **11** Of Earn
14 Epping **15** Abbotsford **16** Sierra **18** Roller
20 Sir Ralph **23** Parade **25** Leone **26** Hill
27 Rhos **29** Dun

Colour party (page 85)
1 'Black Five' **2** Green Park **3** Blue Trains or Blue
Electrics **4** Whitehaven **5** Brown Jack

The National Collection (page 86)
1 Railway catering **2** 'Coppernob' **3** China
4 Pullman Kitchen and Parlour Car **5** It has been
'sectioned' to show its internal fittings and workings
6 West Coast Joint Stock **7** It was the
Dynamometer Car measuring the train's
performance **8** Diesel railcar of 1934 **9** Queen
Adelaide **10** *Columbine* **11** Midland Railway
12 Great Northern Railway **13** 'Atlantic' 4-4-2
14 Butler-Henderson (Hon Eric Butler-Henderson,
son of Sir Alexander Henderson, Lord Faringdon,
respectively director and chairman of the Great
Central) **15** *City of Truro* **16** Butlins **17** SR 'King
Arthur' *Sir Lamiel* **18** No 4003 *Lode Star* **19** No
4073 *Caerphilly Castle* **20** No 1000

Mixed traffic (page 87)
1 Eastfield **2** Edge Hill **3** Inverness **4** Longsight
5 Monument Lane **6** Newton Abbot **7** Newton
Heath **8** Saltley
EEILMNNS = Nine Elms

The end! (page 88)
1 Aberthaw **2** Pwllheli **3** Lambourn **4** Minehead
5 Penzance **6** Llanfair **7** Blenheim **8** Oxenhope
9 Ballater **10** Fortrose
Windermere

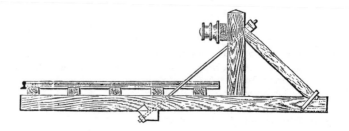